A FLICK OF THE SWITCH

1930-1950

Our Minds Travel Far as Radio Brings the World to Our Homes.

A
FLICK OF THE SWITCH

1930-1950

by

Morgan E. McMahon

First Edition

Published by   Vintage Radio

Production by H. Juhl, Graphic Art Services, Santa Fe Springs, CA.
Photo processing by Gantner Studio, Manhattan Beach, CA.
Printing by Griffin Printing and Lithograph Co., Inc., Glendale, CA.

PHOTO CREDITS

We sincerely thank a number of organizations and people for permission to reproduce materials which enriched this book. All rights are reserved by the following:

American Radio Relay League: QST Magazine.

Andrea Radio Corporation: Miss Camille Andrea; historical materials.

Automatic Radio: G. E. Lyall: Historical materials.

Caldwell-Clements: Radio Retailing, Radio and Television Retailing.

Chicago Tribune — New York Times Syndicate, Incorporated: Little Orphan Annie. ©

Culver Pictures, Incorporated: Just Plain Bill, One Man's Family, Hindenburg disaster.

Electronics Magazine: Daniel A. McMillan, III, historical materials.

Georgia-Pacific Corporation, Hopper Paper Division: Richardson M. Bentley; cover art, personality vignettes, historical materials.

KFI Radio 640: Shirley Palmer; historical materials.

Magnavox Consumer Electronics Company: Miss Judy Cooper; historical materials.

Motorola Incorporated: Ms. Phyllis Grethe; historical materials.

Philco-Ford: William E. Denk; historical materials.

RCA: William C. Hittinger, Ms. Frida Schubert; historical materials.

U.S. Army Communications Museum: Edmond J. Norris; historical materials.

U.S. Navy Bureau of Ships and Office of Naval History: historical materials.

TWA Ambassador: Roy J. Dunlap; historical materials.

Wrather Corporation: Stanley Stunnell; Lone Ranger ©

Ziff-Davis Publishing Company: Jerry Schneider; Radio News, Radio and Television News.

76- 351632

FIRST EDITION

Published by Vintage Radio,
Box 2045, Palos Verdes Peninsula, California, 90274.

ISBN Number   0-914126-09-1 (Hard-cover)
                      0-914126-10-5 (handbook)

4

"I have in mind a plan of development which would make radio a household utility in the same sense as a piano or a phonograph. The idea is to bring music into the home by wireless. A radio telephone transmitter having a range of say 25 to 50 miles can be installed . . . The receiver can be designed in the form of a 'radio music box' and arranged for several different wavelengths, which should be changeable with the throwing of a single switch or pressing of a single button . . . Baseball scores can be transmitted in the air . . . Receiving lectures at home can be made perfectly audible; also events of National importance can be simultaneously announced and received. This proposition would be especially interesting to farmers . . . They could enjoy concerts, lectures, music, recitals, etc., which may be going on in the nearest city."

— David Sarnoff, 1916, in a memo
to his superior while working
for American Marconi.
(Courtesy RCA)

ACKNOWLEDGEMENTS

This book is dedicated to my wife Gladie McMahon, who kept the wheels of Vintage Radio turning while I worked on this book; to Kathie McMahon, who spent her vacations and holidays assembling information for this book; and to Kelly McMahon, who assisted so well on our many picture-taking expeditions.

This book is enriched by the contributions of a great many people, too numerous to mention individually. I sincerely thank each person who contributed an idea, a bit of information or a photo. Aside from these unsung heroes, most pictures in this book came from our friends listed on Page 4 and from the collections of Brent Dingman, Earl England, Hank Hartfield, Louie Irvine, Delton Lee Johnson, Henry Long, Morgan McMahon, John Porter, Ken & Shelia Smith, Richard Smith, Chuck Seidel and Carl Sivertson.

I've received great help and encouragement from a number of fine organizations, including the American Radio Relay League, Antique Radio Club of America, Antique Wireless Association, Indiana Historical Radio Society, Old-Old Timers Club, Radio Club of America and Society of Wireless Pioneers.

I am especially indebted to Hal and Sharon Juhl for many hours of intensive labor to get this book to the printer, and to Dick Bentley of Georgia-Pacific Corporation for his contributions and encouragement.

Bob Morris, W2LV, helped greatly with a compilation of amateur radio hardware for this book. I have Don Elliott to thank for extensive written materials on the story of amateur radio and on World War II military radio-electronics.

ARRL and QST magazine contributed much valuable history.

My thanks to TRW, Incorporated for maintaining our consulting relationship while I was engrossed in researching, writing and publishing this book.

SPECIAL NOTICE

Dates shown in the photo captions are the year of introduction, if known, or the model year. Sets may have been introduced the year previous to the model year. Prices shown are those at the time of introduction, with tubes but without peripheral items such as speakers, headsets and batteries.

CONTENTS

Television's Early Dream; First "Commercial" set, Offered by Jenkins in 1930.

CHAPTER I
WELCOME TO YESTERYEAR

A flick of the switch — that's all it took to summon the new genie of radio entertainment. In this book we take you back to those days when radio was a miraculous new experience, days of wooden radios and pioneering spirit. We'll help you meet old friends, like Just Plain Bill and the Lone Ranger. We'll look in awe at the electronic wonders of World War II. We'll meet old friends, like Kukla, Fran and Ollie. The past joins the present as you spend happy hours browsing through these pages.

THE OLD DAYS

Radio is very new in the great span of human history. James Clerk Maxwell showed it was theoretically possible in 1865. Heinrich Hertz demonstrated the sending and receiving of radio waves in 1887. Guglielmo Marconi set up the first commercial radio station in 1899 between ships and the shore. Commercial radio broadcasting started in 1920, but really convenient plug-in A-C home radios didn't exist until 1927. Commercial TV sets were first available in 1938, though the television industry didn't get its true start until 1946. FM was invented in 1933, and became the music lover's radio after World War II. Actually the "golden days" of radio broadcasting and the accomplishment of television as a great broadcasting medium occurred within the time span of this book, from 1930 to 1950.

We can easily trace the history of radio communication. We find that wireless transmission was experimental, amateur, and commercial up to 1920. Radio reached the point of a thriving young broadcast industry by 1930. It became a booming industry and a part of everyday life by 1940. By 1950 television had reached the state of vigorous adolescence the radio had attained twenty years earlier.

We can also trace the path of radio's "hardware". From 1900 to 1920 the state of the radio art went from crude spark apparatus to vacuum tube equipment. By 1930 there were radios in many homes. By 1940 there was a radio in every home and in

9

Radio takes to the OPEN ROAD

RADIO NEWS, JANUARY 1930

some automobiles. By 1950 there were radios in every home, a radio in almost every automobile, and television sets in many homes.

The art, science, and industry called "electronics" had its beginning in the 1930 to 1950 era. In the 1930's it was limited to operations formerly done by people, such as opening doors, sorting big tomatoes from little ones, weighing products, and counting prunes. World War II gave electronics a tremendous surge, resulting in very sophisticated equipment such as radar, sonar, proximity fuses, and loran. The great computer revolution began in the latter 1940's, beginning with ENIAC in 1946, followed by the IBM 604, EDVAC, CPC-II and SEAC.

About the same time, in 1948, an event took place that would rock the worlds of technology and society. This was the invention of the transistor, which made truly large, complex, reliable machines available. Invention of the transistor has opened new vistas in radio and electronics, all the way from handy $4.50 radios to radars that can be held in your hand. However, its impact by 1950 was almost zero, and plays no part in our book.

Amateur radio played a very important part through all the years of the development of radio. Much of the early technical progress was made by people who were not being paid for their efforts. Most early radio operators and engineers were self-trained through working with their amateur stations. Through the years radio amateurs have been heroes in times of national disasters, establishing contact with the outside world after flood, fire, or storm. The amateur community also was the source for trained people when defense emergencies such as World War I and World War II arose. The radio "Ham" stands as a contributor to progress alongside the technical giants, the great industrial laboratories, government projects and university research.

THIS BOOK

This book picks up in 1930 where our original pictorial his-television broadcasting, which had the greatest effect on most people over these years. We talk about the personalities and broadcast programs of the era. Then we go into radio and television sets, which an archeologist might call the "artifacts" of the past. We go on to record the times and hardware of the radio era. We go on to record the times and hardware of the radio amateur, who is such a key character in the drama of radio-electronics progress. Having visited the radio Ham, we move on to the professional radioman. The radioman can be the poor guy in your neighborhood who tried to squeak out a living repairing radios for people who thought he charged too much. He could have been part of the broadcasting community. He could have been in the world of commercial communications, particularly aboard the ships that plied the seven seas. Next we move into the hobby of radio collecting, showing how to start a hobby that can give you a lot of fun and great satisfaction on either a beer or a champagne budget. This hobby might be a very rewarding investment. We conclude the book with a section about what makes radio "tick", to help you understand the inner workings of these wondrous devices you are playing with.

There are companion books to this one. "Vintage Radio" is the same kind of book, covering the years from the beginning of radio up through 1929; S. Gernsback's "1927 Radio Encyclopedia" gives the reader a very good picture of radio technology as it was in the mid-1920's; The "Radio Collectors Guide" is a data book describing radios built between 1920 and 1932, showing 4000 set models and 50,000 pieces of data; "Most-Often-Needed Radio Diagrams" shows the actual radio circuits for sets built from 1926 through 1938, and we have circuit books available for other years. We will be publishing other books in the future. In particular, we will have pictorial radio and television reference books going into more sets and more detail than we can cover in this one book. We will publish a book on how to restore these fine classic sets once you have acquired them. We will come up with other books as you, our customer, make your wants and needs known. Please write to let us know what books you would like to see in the future, and to make sure you are on our mailing list. Mail to Vintage Radio, Box 2045, Palos Verdes Peninsula, California 90274.

And now – – – enjoy your book!

1. "The Perfect Fool" -- Ed Wynn
2. "Burns and Allen Show" -- George Burns and Gracie Allen
3. "You Bet Your Life" -- Groucho Marx
4. Fred Waring
5. "Jack Benny Show" -- Rochester (Eddie Anderson) and Jack Benny
6. Ben Bernie
7. Paul Whiteman
8. "Bob Hope Show" -- Bob Hope -- Jerry Colonna
9. H. V. Kaltenborn
10. "Hollywood Hotel" -- Francis Langford -- Dick Powell
11. Johnny "Call For Philip Morris"
12. Edgar Bergen and Charlie McCarthy
13. "The Happiness Boys" -- Billy Jones -- Ernie Hare
14. "Metropolitan Opera" -- Milton Cross
15. Babe Ruth -- Graham McNamee
16. "Kollege of Musical Knowledge" -- Kay Kyser
17. "Baby Snooks" -- Fanny Brice
18. Will Rogers
19. "NBC Symphony" -- Arturo Toscanini
20. "One Man's Family"

COURTESY OF
KFI, RADIO 640

The Nation's
Most Powerful
Radio Station

21. Rudy Vallee
22. "Lum and Abner" -- Chet Lauck -- Norris Goff
23. "Henry Aldrich" -- Ezra Stone -- Jackie Kelk
24. "Blondie and Dagwood" -- Arthur Lake -- Penny Singleton
25. "The Fred Allen Show"-- Portland Hoffa -- Jack Benny -- Fred Allen -- Mary Livingston
26. "The Railroad Hour" -- Gordon MacRae
27. Jimmy Fidler
28. "Vic and Sade" -- Arthur Van Harvey -- Billy Idelson -- Bernadine Flynn
29. "Amos and Andy" -- Freeman Gosden -- Charles Correll
30. "The Goldbergs" -- Gertrude Berg
31. "Amateur Hour" -- Major Bowes
32. "National Barn Dance"
33. Glenn Miller
34. "Eddie Cantor Show" -- Eddie Cantor -- Ted Husing
35. "Fibber McGee and Molly" -- Marion Jordan -- Jim Jordan
36. "Information Please" -- Oscar Levant -- John Kieran
37. Bing Crosby -- Boswell Sisters
38. Jimmy Durante

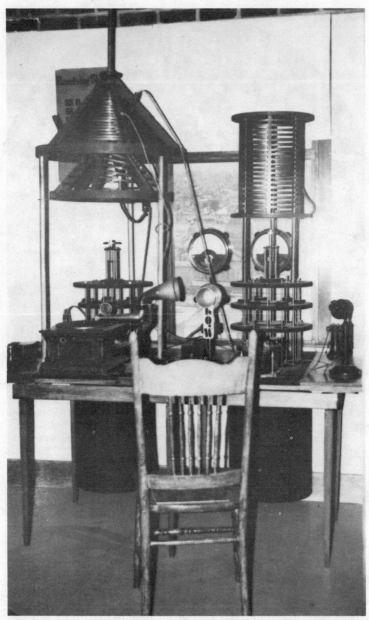

Original radio station KQW, set up by Charles D. Herrold in 1921. Now at Foothill College Electronic Museum, Los Altos, Ca. Prof. Herrold started broadcasting in 1909 using modulated sparks, with his students as the audience.

CHAPTER II
BROADCASTING

It was 1919. Dr. Frank Conrad spoke and people listened. He played music and people listened. The miracle was that he was doing it with radio. This was the beginning of the most important change in communications since the invention of the printing press. This was radio broadcasting!

True, others like Lee DeForest, Reginald Fessenden, Thomas Clark and Charles D. Herrold had tried broadcasting as far back

17

Although Seldom Heard Of, These Men Make Broadcasts Realistic

Scene in the Sound Effects Studio, where these wide-awake young fellows, happy in the knowledge that they are adding to your enjoyment of the radio programs, are busily engaged making the sounds of train and boat whistles, horses galloping, airplanes buzzing, chains rattling, the bustle of traffic, etc., to accompany the oral text of a broadcast playlet. Theirs is not an easy task, as they have to listen-in with headphones for their cues, which must be followed immediately by the proper sound, made in the proper way upon the correct "gadgets."

as 1906. But now the time was right, and Frank Conrad had that missing ingredient, an audience! Westinghouse took his station over in time for the 1920 Warren G. Harding election broadcasts, and Pittsburgh's station KDKA was on the air.

All stations were required to transmit on the same frequency at first, and broadcasting was a mess. In 1923 the Government allocated a band of frequencies, and broadcasting was on its way. There was still one big problem, though; early broadcast receivers required messy batteries and were tricky to operate. A-C radio tubes were introduced in 1927 and radio became a common household friend along with toasters, electric heaters and curling irons.

By 1930 we had a regular stream of radio "visitors" to our homes. During the mid-1920's radio was looked at mostly as a vehicle for music, for humor, and for news. Music, radio's strongest suit, had many top performers, such as Bing Crosby, Kate Smith, Miss Vaughn DeLeath, and Joseph M. White, the "Silver Masked Tenor". Bing Crosby's and Miss DeLeath's "crooning" styles were ideal for getting the most out of the limited capabilities of 1920's radio transmitters. Big bands were given a tremendous boost by radio in the 1920's, much to the delight of bandleaders like Vincent Lopez, Rudy Vallee, and Paul Whiteman. The Voice of Firestone started its many years' run in 1929.

The Happiness Boys started radio's first big humor show in 1921, and continued their run until 1939. Ed Wynn made the first broadcast of a stage show in 1922, a very successful presentation of "The Perfect Love." "Roxy" (Sam Rothafel) had a fine radio variety show going by 1930. Freeman Gosda and Charles Correll's "Amos 'n Andy" was already a national favorite by then.

One-shot guest appearances were very important in broadcasting and brought such immortals as Will Rogers to the people. Will Rogers, probably the greatest of all American homey philosophers, first went on radio in 1922. He made special appearances all through the years until his accidental death in 1935, and his "I never met a man I didn't like" philosophy has stayed with us ever since.

One of the greatest services of radio has been the special broadcast. Sports events, special announcements ("We interrupt

LOUIS/SCHMELING FIGHT

Championship boxing matches in the 1930's had millions of fight fans glued to their radios. In June of 1936, Max Schmeling knocked out Joe Louis, the heavyweight champion of the world, in twelve rounds. Nazi Germany was exuberant. Hitler was enthralled. When the rematch came up June 22, 1938, the whole United States was eager to find out if a countryman, a Negro detested by Hitler's "superrace" could regain his title from the superbly conditioned German. The fight broadcast was quick and furious, like the bout itself," . . .a right and left to the head . . . a left to the jaw . . .a right to the head . . . and the German is watching carefully . . . Louis measures him . . . a right to the body . . . a left

hook to the jaw . . . and Schmeling is down . . . the count . . . 5 . . . 6 . . . 7 . . . 8 . . . the men are in the ring . . . the fight is over . . . on a technical knockout . . . Max Schmeling is beaten in one round. The time 2 minutes and 4 seconds of the first round . . . . the referee stopped it . . . . the winner and still champion, Joe Louis." Max Schmeling had landed only one good punch in the whole fight. Joe Louis, the "Brown Bomber," said after the match, "I waited two years for this revenge, and now I got it."

But it was also a symbolic victory for all Americans, for democracy and all free people who were about to go to war against Nazi Germany.

this program to....."), political campaigns, special events and disasters have all been part of the radio scene. After all, radio broadcasting started with a special event, coverage of the Warren G. Harding election. We thrilled at the broadcasts of Charles A. Lindberg's triumphant return from France in 1927. We ran the full gamut of emotions as Bruno Richard Hauptmann, kidnapper and killer of Lindbergh's child, was apprehended, and shuddered as Gabriel Heatter gave an eyewitness account of his execution in 1935. We listened in near-disbelief in 1936 as we heard the King of England renounce his throne for an American woman. We were horror-stricken as Max Schmeling of Germany took the World's Heavyweight boxing crown away from Joe Louis, and cheered when our Joe won it back again in 1938.

President Franklin D. Roosevelt made great use of radio in his "Fireside Chat" broadcasts, in which he talked directly to the American people twenty-one times. He solidified a shocked nation as he spoke of "A date that will live in infamy" after the Japanese attack on Pearl Harbor in December, 1941. There were many special announcements as we fought through World War II, as the tide went from defeat and gloom to hope, then to victory. All the world listened as the death of President Roosevelt was announced on April 12, 1945, and as Arthur Godfrey described the funeral procession. In the latter 1940's we listened to the atomic bomb tests, and wondered at the monster we'd created.

Probably the greatest unexpected reaction occurred Hallowe'en eve in 1938, when the Nation panicked as Orson Welles presented H. G. Wells' realistic drama "War of the Worlds" and thousands of people believed we were being invaded by creatures from the planet Mars.

We soon discovered that the "voice of radio" was the announcer, who became the sportscaster, special events broadcaster, and radio newsman. Ted Husing and Graham McNamee emerged as two great announcers, particularly in sports broadcasts and special events. Harry Von Zell has had perhaps the greatest announcing career, spanning from the 1920's to the 1970's and covering the full range of program announcement, sports, news, commercials, and acting assignments. Many announcers emerged as newscasters. Floyd Gibbons and H. V. Kaltenborn were important music and news analysts by 1930. In the 1930's and 1940's there were many more newscasters: Gabriel Heatter, Boake Carter, Elmer Davis, Paul Harvey, Herb Morrison, Drew Pearson, Lowell Thomas and Edward R. Murrow to name a few.

The 1930's saw a parade of stars issuing from our radio speakers. The wonders of their presentations were limited only by our ability to imagine the scene portrayed in word and music. Housewives stopped work to hear their favorite soap operas. They wept as Ma Perkins solved another problem of her embattled friends, or as Just Plain Bill encountered another insurmountable problem and solved it with deft tact. Some of the plots were unbelieveably complicated and would have been "X-rated" if they had appeared in today's movies.

Kids hurried home to eat Wheaties as they listened to Jack Armstrong and tried to amass enough box tops for that secret decoder ring. Beginning in 1933, the Lone Ranger with his faithful friend, Tonto, saved innumerable people's lives, honor and fortunes, then rode away "with a hearty Hi-Yo Silver."

We all relaxed in happy contentment (except when we were rolling on the floor with laughter) from our old-shoe friends like Lum and Abner at the Jot 'Em Down Store, and Vic and Sade with their weird situations that could really happen to any of us. Little Orphan Annie was a favorite of all, and even mother sneaked a listen when she could. Mom and Dad had their evening programs, including music, news, and their favorite comedy hours. Sundays were particularly rich in radio programs, when the whole family was trapped by that magic box in the living room. Those fortunate enough to live in the 1930's and 1940's well-remember listening to Jack Benny, Fred Allen, Burns and Allen, Fibber McGee and Molly, Rudy Vallee, Bob Hope, Graham McNamee, and Fulton Lewis, Jr. There were some remarkable characters like Jerry Collona, and some unforgettable props like Fibber McGee's perpetually-collapsing closet. One of the most unlikely characters (especially for radio) was a ventriloquist's dummy named Charlie McCarthy who brought along his friend, Edgar Bergen. One Man's Family was the perennial favorite of millions of people. Myrt and Marge were the heroines of many a teen-age girl. In later years teen-age girls, and the whole family, enjoyed the adventures of Corliss Archer. On

FDR'S FIRESIDE CHATS

Franklin Delano Roosevelt, inaugurating his New Deal, found a way of communicating to a distraught nation, a nation caught in the grip of a severe depression and headed toward a major war. No national leader had ever established such rapport with his people as FDR achieved through his radio broadcasts. Usually aired after the dinner hour, they became known as the "Fireside Chats." One of these had the largest listening audience in radio history. Here are a few quotes from them.

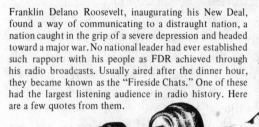

September 30, 1934
"I am not for a return to that definition of liberty under which for many years a free people were being gradually regimented into the service of the privileged few. I prefer and I am sure you prefer that broader definition of liberty under which we are moving forward to a greater freedom, to greater security for the average man than he has ever known before in the history of America."

April 14, 1938
"History proves that dictatorships do not grow out of strong and successful governments, but out of weak and helpless ones. If by democratic methods people get government strong enough to protect them from fear and starvation, their democracy succeeds; but if they do not, they grow impatient. Therefore, the only sure bulwark of continuing liberty is a government strong enough to protect the interests of the people, and a people strong enough and well enough informed to maintain sovereign control over its government."

December 29, 1940
"We must be the great arsenal of democracy."

September 11, 1941
"When you see a rattlesnake poised to strike, you do not wait until he has struck before you crush him."

February 23, 1942
"Never before have we so little time in which to do so much."

the boys' side, Henry Aldrich kept us all laughing. And there were were the mystery stories—Jack, Doc, and Reggie scared the pie out of kids in that great serial drama, I Love A Mystery. Remember Inner Sanctum's creaking door? Then there was the Shadow—"whoo knooows what eevil lurks in the hearts of men? The Shadow knows! Heh Heh Heh! Heh!" There were also the sophisticated mystery programs, like "Mr. and Mrs. North" and "The Thin Man", Other programs, although not so suspense-filled, were entirely enjoyable. Do you recall the Little Theater Off Times Square with Olan Soule', or the people-participation programs, like the granddaddy of them all, Major Bowes' Amateur Hour? Remember the gong that struck terror into the hearts of contestants? It even scared us when somebody got the gong and the hook. Later were the many quiz programs, both of the high-caliber "Quiz Kids" and "Information Please" variety and the ones where just we mortals participated. "Truth or Consequences" was fun for all. "Your Hit Parade" was a tremendously popular radio show, as were the other musical offerings.

We like to remember all the thousands of local radio shows also. Not all of them were national hook-ups. How many of us recall the life-and-death struggle of Dude Martin and his Nevada Night-herders against Stewart Hamblin's Gang? How many of us recall the programs that started "And now it's 11:15 and time for your adventures in sports with Ira Blue"?

What happened to some of these people? What happened to Pic 'n Pat, the great little comedy team of the early 30's? Where did the Lone Ranger and Superman hibernate for all those years before they started to reappear on radio program replays? Some just disappeared, others were preserved on records for twenty years and then were rediscovered. Others made the transition from radio to television.

Television! It took many years to perfect a system for sending radio pictures into every home. When TV did come, it had a tremendous effect. It was something of a shock to discover that Superman looked more like Uncle Ed in his winter woolies than like the noble being we envisioned in our radio imaginations. As television came booming in it usurped our freedom of imagination, but in return for this freedom we were given entire new

Orson Welles' presentation of H. G. Wells' "War of the Worlds" caused a nationwide panic as people took the 1938 Hallowe'en program to be a real emergency broadcast.

Early in World War II, when Edward R. Murrow's *This is London* came over network radio directly from short wave transmitters in England, people listened and reflected. The American public got a first-hand glimpse of Britain's struggle for survival through Murrow's adroit reporting. His choice of subject and style of writing comprised a directness and presence seldom surpassed in radio journalism. Over the crackle and static, the volume fading in and out, the people listened.

"This is London.:"

August 31, 1939. "Tomorrow we shall see the children, the halt, the lame, and the blind going out of Britian's cities. Six hundred and fifty thousand will leave London tomorrow. The exodus will start at 5:30 in the morning. In all, there are three million people to be evacuated in the crowded areas, one million three hundred thousand from London alone. Nine roads out of London and only one way traffic. It's not going to be a pleasant sight."

June 2, 1940. "I talked with pilots as they came back from Dunkirk... They were the cream of the youth of Britain ...They told me of the patrol from which they'd just returned."Six Germans downed. We lost two." "What happened to Eric?" said one. "Oh, I saw him go down along side of one of the destroyers," replied another. ...."Six of us go over," they said, "and we meet twelve Germans. If ten of us go, there's twenty Germans." When the squadron took off, one of them remarked quite casually that he would be back in time for tea."

Sept. 8, 1940. "It was like a shuttle service, the way the German planes came up the Thames, the fires acting as a flare path. Often they were above the smoke. The searchlights bored into that black roof, but couldn't penetrate it. They looked like long pillars supporting a black canopy. Suddenly all the lights dashed off, and a blackness fell right to the ground. It grew cold. We covered ourselves with hay. The shrapnel clicked as it hit the concrete road nearby, and still the German bombers came."

NEWSMAN: EDWARD R. MURROW

vistas of enjoyment, information, and suspense. To many of us the first fuzzy images we saw on our earliest television screens were those of our dear new friends, Kukla, Fran and Ollie. A whole new world of entertainment opened up, where every night was movie night. We could view newsreels fresh off the press, and even see live news event coverage. Sports broadcasting made a fantastic leap ahead; sports events were one area in which the imagination was nowhere near as good as the real thing. This is particularly true when sports events were "recreated" on radio and the announcer rapped the microphone with his pencil to simulate a base hit, and where it was difficult to keep enthusiasm cranked up. Some old radio programs died, but new TV greats like Milton Berle, Ed Sullivan, Sid Caesar, Imogene Coca, and Jackie Gleason, joined successful "retreads" like Jack Benny, Fred Allen, and Bob Hope. Amateur hours failed on a national scale, possibly because there was no way to make the contestants look as romantic as they appeared in the radio listener's imagination.

Radio did not die, however. It became the hand-maiden of the motoring public. Also disc jockeys and talk shows have filled millions of hours of air time over the intervening years. A late innovation (after 1950) was the all-news program where you could get the world news anytime by turning to a particular station.

Radio and television performers were only the "tip of the iceberg." Each person on the air was backed by many writers, technicians, studio support people and administrators. It took an army of people to design and manufacture the equipment used in broadcasting. Radio had to survive and grow as a business, hence there were many businessmen involved, some of whom failed. David Sarnoff and Powel Crosley were men whose far-reaching dreams became the great reality of network broadcasting. Sarnoff started RCA's National Broadcasting Company which became so large that the government later broke its "Red" and "Blue" networks into today's NBC and ABC. An upstart competitor formed in 1927 became CBS, the third major network. American broadcasting has always been run as a self-sufficient industry, working from advertising income; sellers pay for the air time and listeners pay for the programs by listening to the blandishments of the sellers, and presumably buying products. This has been a very effective way to promote products and to keep the wheels of American industry turning. British broadcasting, on the other hand, has always been a government-subsidized operation, paid for by indirect taxation and by government license fees for all radio and television sets. Both ways work, and there are many arguments as to which is better.

Broadcasting can be a very powerful tool for good or for bad. In the United States it has been very jealously guarded as a tool for the truth. The Federal Communications Commission (FCC) is charged with walking the line between freedom and good taste, and has done a good job over the years in this delicate role. Broadcasting could easily become a powerful tool of oppression, so this factor too must be watched. Hitler used it as a tremendous tool to sell his dangerous philosophies.

We can't pretend to cover the history of radio and television broadcasting in this one chapter. There are some very good books available. "A Pictorial History of Radio" by Irving Settle (Grosset & Dunlap, New York, 1967) is a fascinating reference on the programs and personalities of radio broadcasting. A similarly entertaining book on television is "A Pictorial History of Television" by Daniel Blum (Bonanza Books, New York, 1959). For a full listing of all nationally-broadcast programs, 1920-1950, with the names of the actors, see "The Big Broadcast" by Frank Buxton and Bill Owen (The Viking Press, New York, 1972). Ron Lackman's "Remember Radio" (G. P. Putnam's Sons, New York) and Jim Harmon's "The Great Radio Comedians" and "The Great Radio Heroes" (Doubleday & Co., Garden City, N.Y.) are entertaining and informative memory trips. If you're interested in the dynamic history of the broadcast industry, try Erik Barnouw's excellent series "A Tower in Babel," "The Golden Web" and "The Image Empire" (Oxford University Press, N.Y.). Tapes and records of old radio programs are also very enjoyable, and can be found in record shops and in the classified sections of antique periodicals.

Perhaps the role of broadcasting has been best immortalized on the nameplate of some mid-1930's Philco radios. This escutcheon says simply "Music, News, Drama, Comedy, Sports, Education".

HINDENBURG DISASTER

The Hindenburg Zeppelin was built in the early 1930's to meet the increased demand for air-passenger service. It held 72 passengers and twice the volume of gas of its predecessors. It seemed destined to start a new era in airship travel. On the evening of May 6, 1937, the Hindenburg was arriving at Lakehurst, New Jersey, after a successful North Atlantic crossing. The engines were idling and mooring lines had been dropped to the ground crew.

Radio announcer Herbert Morrison of WLS, Chicago, was on the field below reporting to his listeners. Suddenly there was a terrible roar as the hydrogen-filled airship burst into a huge mushroom of flame. Morrison described the terrible scene in a horror-choked voice. He wept as he told of passengers burning or leaping to their deaths, and of ground-crewmen crushed under the twisted, burning hulk.

The tragic explosion of the Hindenburg was possibly the most heart-rending broadcast ever made.

Ruth Russell and Arthur Hughes in Just Plain Bill

Anthony Smythe and Ninetta Ellen in One Man's Family

SOAP OPERAS

Soap Operas—fifteen minutes a day, five days a week—were the greatest orchestration of emotions ever to spellbind a mass audience. The daily miniature dramas kept millions of women misty-eyed over their ironing boards, and had an appeal which tugged at the heartstrings of the menfolk as well.

For many, each episode provided a means of escaping the reality of an era which had its share of real-life ups and downs. No one could offer greater comfort than Ma Perkins (Oxydol's own). No one could inspire the aspirations of the housewife like Mary Noble, Backstage Wife. No real flesh-and-blood woman could face heartbreak and troubles like Stella Dallas. There was no logic more honest and homespun than Just Plain Bill's. The Romance of Helen Trent helped middle-aged women understand their longings, and impractical crackpot-inventor Lorenzo Jones helped some to accept less-than-perfect husbands in a less-than-perfect decade.

Sage advice from Ma Perkins epitomized the soapers, and may be the reason Ma, played by Virginia Payne for 27 years, lasted longer than almost any of the others. On the very last broadcast, at her own Thanksgiving table, Ma's thoughts again turned to the great circle of things. "like the turning of stars in the heavens." Gathered around the table, "laden with the fruits of this good green earth," with her loved ones, she thought, "Oh, someday Fay will be sitting here where I'm sitting, or Evey or Paulette or Janie or Anushka's child. But I find right and peace in that ... I give thanks that I have been given this gift of life, this gift of time, to play my little part."

30

FRED ALLEN — JACK BENNY FEUD

"I'll knock the guy so cold he'll think he's something Admiral Byrd left behind"

"If I had my writers here you wouldn't get away with that"

Radio politely coasted from one tranquil program to another in the early thirties until Jack Benny and Fred Allen interrupted the calm with their famous feud. Off mike, they were the best of friends; on mike, their uncensored insults generated high ratings for both programs. Fan mail poured in. Many listeners took the feud seriously. Jack challenged Fred to a boxing match. After weeks of radio build-up, the fight broadcast was held Sunday, March 14, 1937. Next to one of FDR's fireside chats, a survey reported this program to be one of the top rated programs of all time.

The feud—a radio battle of words rather than fists—called for lines from Fred Allen like, "I'll knock that guy so cold he'll think he's something Admiral Byrd left behind," "He's a pan dowdy with skin on," or "Benny's stomach hangs down like a Jello knapsack."

Flagstaff Openshaw, Senator Claghorn, Mrs. Nussbaum and Titus Moody, among others, were his regular cast of characters. Titus Moody, a dour New Englander, commented suspiciously about radio, "I don't hold with furniture that talks."

Jack Benny, radio's best known and beloved comedian, utilized a completely different approach to his program, one more akin to today's situation comedy on television.

His cast of characters played themselves, as did Benny; Don Wilson, the announcer, Dennis Day, the singer, Phil Harris, the bandleader, Mary Livingston, Benny's wife, and the most famous role of all, the valet Rochester. This approach achieved great believability with plots revolving around everyday events, such as trying to round up the gang for a rehearsal of the weekly show, a device used countless times.

Jack's reputed stinginess led to one episode in which he was accosted by a robber who threatened, "Your money or your life." After the longest silence ever broadcast, during which the audience laughter must also have set some sort of record, the robber yelled, "Well?" Finally, Jack answered, "I'm thinking it over."

31

Big-time radio fought a losing battle for survival.

Mom, Dad and youngsters listening to war news, World War II.

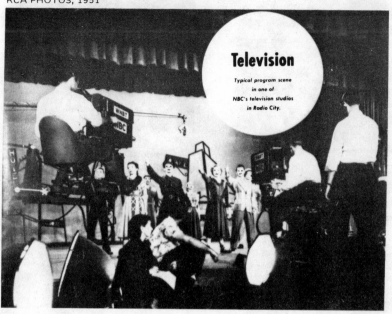

Television

Typical program scene
in one of
NBC's television studios
in Radio City.

Hero of early TV experimentation was Felix the Cat shown here facing bright lights in an NBC test.

Scene from "Susan and God," starring Gertrude Lawrence, first great actress to appear on TV.

Fran Allison and friends in
NBC's Kukla, Fran and Ollie,
with Burr Tilstrom.

Families were captured by the wonders of television.

Robert Montgomery, film star, turned his acting and production talents
to television with great success, 1940's.

First televised football game, Fordham v.s. Waynesburg in New York, September 30, 1939

First televised baseball game, Brooklyn v.s. Cincinnati at Ebbets Field, August 26, 1939.

Now — Radio *for* Every Room

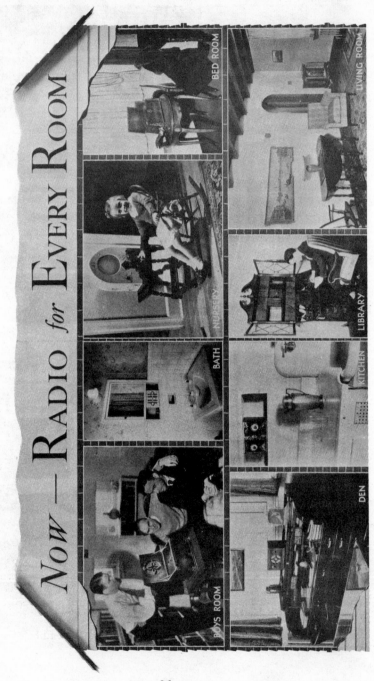

BED ROOM

LIVING ROOM

NURSERY

LIBRARY

BATH

KITCHEN

BOYS ROOM

DEN

CHAPTER III
HOME RADIO AND TV

The living-room radio was a gathering place for the whole family in the 1930's and 1940's, bringing the outside world into every home. These Golden Years continued to the end of the era, when television's radio-picture took over.

Maybe you remember the family grouped around that highly-polished living-room radio listening to a favorite Sunday-evening program. The old folks were dozing in their chairs, waking enough to smile or laugh with the group as the younger folks broke into raucous laughter. Dad sat nursing his pipe, his eyes lighting with amusement at the programs. Mom knitted or crocheted, or worked with that needlepoint job that seemed to take forever. The big kids were sprawled on the rug looking at the radio but seeing great adventures in far-away places. The little kids spent much time being shushed as they disturbed the rapt concentration of the older folks.

If you remember the golden days of radio broadcasting, you can remember the radio, that monument to communications and display-piece of family wealth. You recall looking at the other families' radio and mentally comparing it to your own.

What about that old radio that once was the center of your leisure life? Chances are it still exists somewhere. Maybe it's still in your attic or basement. If so, you are one of the lucky ones. If you don't still have the faithful old beast, you can probably find one like it and discover a very pleasant trip back to those days.

Maybe you recall the old "compact" radio that sat on the living-room table, and was retired to your bedroom when you got that big beautiful console job. Even later, you bought your first inexpensive little AC-DC set, and one day found yourself with table radios in almost every room of the house. The ultimate in little baby sets came when you could buy the midget radio for $9.95. You probably remember listening to your bed-side set as you fell asleep, waking in the wee small hours to hear its gentle buzz and crashes of static from far-away storms, as the warm glow of its light cast gentle shadows in your room.

Do you recall that first auto radio, the one with the tuning head and the cables running down to that big box on the firewall? Wasn't it a thrill to hear words and music as you chugged down tree-lined country roads? Do you remember the risk of running your battery down as you listened to soft music in the moonlight at your favorite parking spot?

If you are too young to remember, you can still recapture these early days by turning on an old radio and listening to replays of early programs like "I Love a Mystery," "Jack Armstrong," or "One Man's Family."

All these radios from the magnificent console to the tiniest "junker" are important pieces of our modern heritage and are worthy of the collector. In this chapter we assemble an army of wonderful old sets for your inspection. Perhaps you will find the old set you remember so well. Perhaps you are a collector who will want to use our book as a guide to filling the holes in your assembly of historical old hardware. We are sure you'll get a chuckle out of some of the weird old sets, such as the Mickey Mouse radio and the "handsome" Charlie McCarthy piece.

A word of explanation of our "mug shots" of these old sets is in order: Date shown is usually that when the particular model appeared in nation-wide magazines. Sometimes it is the model year, in which case the set may have been introduced in the summer or fall of the previous year. We have arranged each manufacturer's sets by year of introduction, rather than by model number. This way, it is much easier to trace trends in sets from the heavy TRF lunkers of 1930 to the lightweight superheterodyne of 1950. Prices shown are the advertised price when the set was introduced, including tubes. Model numbers are the greatest help in exchanging information on radio sets. They weren't always assigned in numerical order, so you're taking a chance if you assume a lower model number means an older set. Sometimes you'll find the same chassis model showing up in different cabinets, or the same cabinet housing different chassis models. You may also find the same model number popping up years apart on completely different sets, as with the 1931 and 1938 Philco 70B's.

If you're interested in acquiring historical old radio sets as conversation pieces, or in starting a collection, you'll find Chapter

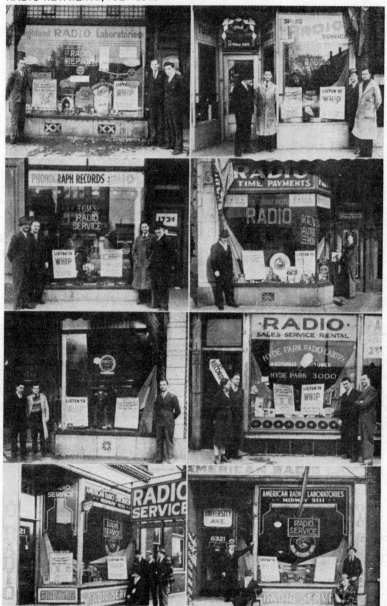

Local shops were the front-line troops in radio's dynamic growth.

PIONEER F-M EQUIPMENT

Major Edwin Howard Armstrong and his assistant Harry Houck pioneered the development of practical frequency modulation (FM) equipment in 1933, inventing the circuitry and demonstrating atop the Empire State Building.

PHASE MODULATOR FOR ARMSTRONG'S
EMPIRE STATE BUILDING EXPERIMENTS.

TRANSMITTER R-F MODULE USED IN
INITIAL F-M TESTS.

1946 ZENITH AM-FM
COMMEMORATIVE RADIO
"THE MAJOR"
COVERING BOTH THE OLD
(42-50MC)
AND NEW (88-108MC)
F-M BANDS, PLUS A-M

VII to be of great help. If you're interested in delving into even earlier days of wireless and radio, we recommend our book Vintage Radio, 1887-1929.

RADIO RECEIVERS

By 1930, almost 3 million radios were being sold each year. These were mostly A-C radios with the old tuned-radio-frequency (TRF) circuits. RCA controlled the vastly superior superheterodyne circuit and did not release it to other manufacturers until the 1931 model year. The broadcast band was 500 to 1500 Kc using amplitude modulated (AM) radio waves. This band is still the one most used in home and automobile radios, but now extends to 1600 Kc.

Short-wave listening became very popular in the early 1930's, and by 1933 almost everyone wanted to have the short-wave bands and compete with their friends to see what station, farthest away, they could boast about to their friends. True high-fidelity, in terms of todays "audiophile", was not a big thing by the end of this era, although manufacturers of quality sets strove for high-quality reproduction. Labyrinth speakers, tuned enclosures, and multiple speaker systems had been introduced by the 1940's, but the quality of AM transmission and of available recording media did not require truly good high-frequency response. However, the quality of FM and the appearance of high-fidelity micro-groove records spawned the high-fidelity craze which began early in the 1950's.

In 1930 the majority of broadcast receivers sold were of the console type. However, as the depression deepened and purses grew thinner, people were forced to buy less expensive sets. The industry responded by creating the smaller sets known variously as cathedral, compact, or depression radios. In 1933 74% of all radios sold were table models. AC-DC sets, first introduced by International Kadette in 1931, made possible a drastic drop in prices and the dream of a "radio in every room in the house" became a reality. Plastic radios, also pioneered by Kadette, permitted a further swing to large volumes of inexpensive sets. Total radio sales were about 3.8 million sets in 1930 growing to 7.6 million in 1937, and 9.7 million sets in 1949.

41

Automobile radios became a reality in 1930, pioneered by Motorola, Crosley, Zenith, RCA, Philco, and Automatic Radios. Only 34,000 auto radios were sold in 1930, but these sales grew to 1.4 million sets in 1936. Auto radios were ideal for alleviating the boredom of automobile driving, and auto radio advertisers inferred that all kinds of romantic interludes were available to the young man who had a radio in his car. Typically, auto radio ads showed a young man zipping along in wild abandon with a beautiful young lady at his side.

In 1933 Major Edwin H. Armstrong invented frequency modulation (FM). Frequency modulation has the advantage of being almost immune to the static that bothers AM, and is excellent for high-fidelity reproduction. It's disadvantage is that it requires a wider frequency band, so that the FM bands are at a high frequency where long-distance broadcasting is poor.

In 1940 the Federal Communications Commission established a 42-50 Mc band, and 400,000 FM receivers were tuned to 25 commercial stations by the end of 1941. In 1944 the FCC set a new FM band of 88-108 Mc, which is still in use. The lower frequency band was phased out. By 1950 most high-quality radios had both AM and FM bands.

Portable radios were originally heavy and awkward, and were more of a stunt than a convenience. By 1939, however, the younger generation was enthusiastically gobbling up the production of cloth-covered portable radios. By 1946 plastic portable radios were selling by the hundreds of thousands. The greatest revolution, that of the transistor, did not occur until late in the 1950's.

Radio production did not die as the television revolution swept on. In 1949 for instance, 2.8 million television sets were built, but almost 10 million radio sets were built in the same time. The format of radio broadcasting changed a great deal, however, as television took over our entertainment programs. News programs, talk shows, and disc jockeys took over the air waves of the AM band aimed particularly at automobile radios and youth relaxing away from television sets. Also, FM stations were the major source of high-quality music which was becoming more and more important to the listeners. We could twist Mark Twain's famous saying by stating that "reports of the death of radio had been greatly exaggerated".

TELEVISION RECEIVERS

Television, one of the miracles of our modern age, actually has its roots more than a hundred years ago when man first thought of sending pictures over wires. In 1847, Frederick Bakewell sent line drawings over telegraph wires using his "facsimile" system. In 1881, Shelford Bidwell, another Englishman, sent pictures of actual still scenes over wires giving what we might call "still television." In 1884, Paul Nipkow was issued a German patent on a television system of sending moving pictures over wires. The basic system concept is the same as we use today, although of course the modern equipment is far more sophisticated. Nipkow's picture consisted of a "raster" of lines made by a whirling disc of pinholes. The transmitter used a disc and a photocell to generate the electrical impulses corresponding to the picture. The receiver used a light source which was varied by the electrical signal, and which was synchronized with the transmitter using another whirling disc. Actual television using the "Nipkow disc" was demonstrated by John L. Baird in England in April 1925 over a short distance. In June 1925, C. Francis Jenkins demonstrated true television over a distance of 25 miles in Washington, D.C. In 1927, the Bell Telephone Laboratories demonstrated a large-screen television on a two-foot-square screen over a distance of 320 miles by radio and telephone lines. All these experiments still used the Nipkow disc. The use of cathode ray tubes for television was investigated by the Germans Lux and Deickmann in 1906, and was discussed in the magazine Nature in 1908 by Campbell-Swinton. Use of the primitive Nipkow disc, however, was the main thrust of television into the early 1930's. Various promoters were pushing Nipkow disc television and attempted to make it a commercial product. However, the mechanical system just wasn't good enough.

Scanning-disc television reached its peak in about 1932, but it was apparent that it would never attain true commercial quality.

Fortunately, Philo Farnsworth and V. K. Zworykin were experimenting with electronic television as early as the early 1920's. Zworykin filed his iconoscope television tube patent application in 1923. Farnsworth demonstrated the first true all-electronic

DEVELOPMENT OF TELEVISION CONCEPTS

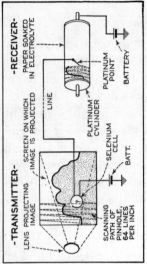

FIGURE 2. BIDWELL'S "STILL TELEVISION." 1881

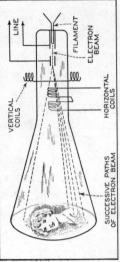

FIGURE 4. CAMPBELL-SWINTON CATHODE RAY RECEIVER. 1908

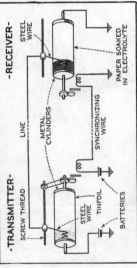

FIGURE 1. BAKEWELL'S FACSIMILE SYSTEM—1847

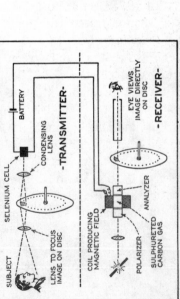

FIGURE 3. NIPKOW'S DISC TELEVISION SYSTEM. 1884

Mechanical television was the only available scheme until the early 1930's, even though the idea of cathode-ray tube (kinescope) TV was many years old. Philo T. Farnsworth and Vladimir Zworykin made electronic TV real in this country, and it was independently developed in Europe.

cathode-ray tube TV in 1929, and Zworykin demonstrated his first sophisticated TV system at Westinghouse in the same year, using the "kinescope" cathode ray tube. John Logi Baird demonstrated sequential field color television in 1928, and Bell Labs demonstrated color television in 1929. However, the sequential field system is not truly useable. By 1935 it was apparent that the system of Farnsworth and Zworykin using the iconoscope and kinescope principles would be the successful television technology. In that year, regular German television programs were broadcast, with 180 lines per frame, 25 frames per second.

In 1936 the British Broadcasting Company (BBC) broadcast both the scanning-disc television with 240 lines and 405-line Marconi all-electronic systems in regular programs. In the same year, RCA demonstrated a successful all-electronic system, and the American standard was set at 440 lines per frame, 30 frames per second, 60 fields per second. In 1937, the British dumped the Baird system and swung completely to the electronic system. That same year in the United States, the Federal Communications Commission established 19 channels, each 6 megacycles wide, from 44 to 294 megacycles. The same year, Zworykin demonstrated an 8-foot by 10-foot projection television using the cathode-ray tube. Late 1938 and 1939 saw a major push to get the public to buy television sets. Much publicity was given to television at the New York and San Francisco World Fairs. Dumont introduced their set in December '38, followed by RCA, Belmont, Philco, ATC, and smaller enterpreneurs. However, costs were very high, and there was very little programmed television available. In addition, industry and FCC standards were still in a state of change, and any television set was in danger of immediate obsolescence. The state of television enthusiasm was very short-lived, and television did not really take off as a major industry until after World War II. In 1941, the FCC set the now-familiar TV standards of amplitude-modulated video with suppressed lower side band, with FM sound. Sound and picture carriers were 4.5 megacycles apart, and the frame was 525 lines, 30 frames per second, interlaced with 60 fields per second. There were 21 licensed commercial TV stations in July 1941, but World War II brought television to a halt. Television took off explosively after the war. By mid-1947 there were 50,000 TV sets in the United

States, and 150,000 sets by the year's end. There were over a million television sets in use by the end of 1948, almost 4 million by the end of 1949, and almost 10 million by the end of 1950. These were paced by the existence of 13 TV stations in latter 1947, 51 stations by the end of 1949, and 107 stations by the end of 1950. Television had indeed become a major force in our lives by the end of that decade.

The big battle for color television began in 1941. CBS demonstrated their field sequential color TV system to the press in early 1946. Dumont demonstrated color-tube TV that same year. RCA demonstrated large projection-type color television in 1947. By 1949, the color TV battle had narrowed to the CBS field sequential system on one hand and the fully-compatible "dot sequential" color TV by RCA on the other hand. ("Fully-compatible" means that the color programs can be seen in black-and-white on the older non-color sets.) Color Television, Inc. helped set the technicolor pace, but didn't have the resources to become a major competitor. Comparative tests were held by the FCC in 1949 and 1950. FCC first adopted the field sequential system, but in 1953 switched to the RCA dot-sequential system now in use.

With this introduction, we'll leave you to wander through the halls of our "museum." These pages are the largest single assemblage of 1930-1950 classic radio set pictures ever published, and are the best historical and collector's reference you'll find.

We will publish more comprehensive directories on each subject in the future, so keep in touch!

RADIO NEWS,
OCTOBER 1948

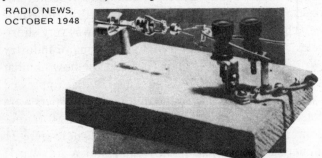

Next-generation revolution: The transistor was discovered in 1948, and became the miracle device of the 1950's.

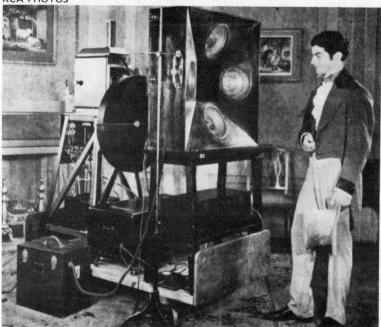

How it worked: Arc lamp at left fed light through a rotating disc, scanning the subject with a moving spot of light. Large photocells picked up the reflected light and modulated the transmitter.

A light source, flickering from the received transmitter signal, was fed through a rotating disc with a spiral hole pattern reproducing the original image.

ADMIRAL CORP.
(CONTINENTAL RADIO & TELEVISION CO.)

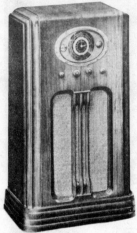

◊ MODEL AM 786
11 TUBES $69.75
1936

MODEL AM 787
"TILT-TUNER"
11 TUBES $79.50 ◊
1936

◊ MODEL 930-16R
"TILT-TUNER"
16 TUBES 1937

MODEL 113-5A
"MAGNASCOPE" DIAL
113-5A BLACK $16.95 ◊
114-5A WALNUT $17.95
115-5A IVORY $19.95
1938

Admiral

AMERICA'S SMARTEST PORTABLE RADIOS

for

1940

Featuring the Automatic Power Switch . . . New R. F. Circuit . . . Full Tone Speakers . . . Special Output Tube . . . Temperature Control Aperture . . . Aeroscope Magic Antenna.

Model 33-F5—5 tube AC-DC or 1½ volt battery operated superhet with tuning range 540 to 1550 K. C.

Model 34-F5—Chassis same as Model 33-F5.

Model 37-G6—6 tube AC-DC or 1½ volt battery operated superhet with tuning range 540 to 1550 K.C.

Model 35-G6—Chassis same as model 37-G6. Brown leatherette cabinet with detachable cover has leather carrying handle. (See radio in picture with girl).

See Your Jobber

CONTINENTAL RADIO & TELEVISION CORP.

3800 W. Cortland St., Chicago
Export Office: 116 Broad St., N. Y.

ADMIRAL CORP.
(CONTINENTAL RADIO & TELEVISION CO.)

MODEL 123-5E
INTRODUCED AS 2-BAND SET
WITH MARBLED CASE AT $15.00,
THEN CHANGED TO 1-BAND
◊ PLAIN CASE $9.95 SPECIAL
5 TUBES   1938

MODEL 361-5Q ◊
5 TUBES $9.95
1939

MODEL 8C11
AM-FM-TV
◊ 10" PICTURE
$499.95   1948

MODEL 7C73
AM-FM $289.95 ◊
9 TUBES   1947

MODEL 19A11SN
◊ 6" PICTURE
18 TUBES   1949

32X36—(12½" Tube). Admiral 3-way TV combination in traditional walnut or mahogany. Walnut, **$379.95**

32X27—(12½" Tube). New television combination sensation in mahogany or blonde cabinet. Mahogany, **$399.95**

39X17—(19" Tube). Superb new TV combination in modern mahogany or blonde. Mahogany, **$695.00**

32X15—(12½" Tube). Thrilling new television combination. Walnut or mahogany. In walnut only **$299.95**

29X16—(19" Tube). Ultra modern mahogany or blonde television console. In walnut, a sensation at **$495.00**

12X12—(12½" Tube). New low price table television sensation. In smart mahogany color cabinet, **$179.95**

26X46—(16" Tube). Admiral TV combination. Rectangular tube. Walnut or mahogany. In walnut, **$299.95**

Prices slightly higher south and west . . . subject to change without notice. Tax extra.

51

AIRLINE
MONTGOMERY WARD & CO.

MODEL 05B-A
5 TUBES   1934 APP.

MODEL 62-606 SERIES A
5 TUBES   1938 MY

1938 APP.

MODEL 345
6 TUBES   BATTERY
1941 APP.

MODEL 84BR 1065B
5 TUBES   BATTERY   1946

RADIO-PHONO
MODEL 17A 80
62-2709
7 TUBES   1941

MODEL 5D8-1
5 TUBES   AC-DC

AMERICAN BOSCH
(AMERICAN BOSCH MAGNETO CORP., UNITED AMERICAN BOSCH CORP.)

VIBRO-POWER
MODEL 350 (AC)
MODEL 355 (AC-DC)
5 TUBES $37.50
1933 ◊

◊ VIBRO-POWER
MODEL 360T ALL-WAVE $62.50
MODEL 370T BCST. $52.50
7 TUBES   1933

VIBRO-POWER
MODEL 360S ALL-WAVE $94.50 ◊
MODEL 370S BCST. $84.50
7 TUBES   1933

◊ AUTOMATIC MAESTRO 670C
9 TUBES LW-BC-SC
1936

AUTOMATIC MAESTRO 660T ◊
7 TUBES ALL-WAVE
1936

The AMRAD SON-DO Model. A new electric phonograph and radio combination incorporating the latest eight tube AMRAD Screen Grid, Neutrodyne chassis and the new AMRAD Type 249 Dynamic power speaker in a cabinet pronounced the most beautiful ever produced. It contains two wells for records. Priced at $240.00, less tubes.

GALILEO ... believer in the infinite mystery of the heavens, was ridiculed by sages of his generation. He was one of the founders of experimental science . . . and Italy smiled. He sought a thing which could not be.

High in the tower of Saint Mark, when his skeptical friends slept, Galileo searched the uncharted heavens with crude astronomical instruments and plucked new planets from infinity, through the telescope he had dreamed to a reality.

Radio's restless 'search of space and this same infinity of blue, is singularly paralleled. There was destined to be one, of all the others, that, with splendid vision, should bring new miracles to bear . . . new worlds of speech and song from out the vastness of starry nights . . . coupled with surpassing beauty of appearance and superlative performance . . . AMRAD RADIO.

The AMRAD RONDEAU Model. A magnificent cabinet enlivened with exquisite carved decorations. The set is the latest AMRAD eight tube Screen Grid, Neutrodyne chassis. The new AMRAD Type 249 Dynamic power speaker is incorporated. Automatic volume control maintains a practically uniform volume. Priced at $150.00, less tubes.

AMRAD DIVISION of
THE CROSLEY RADIO CORPORATION

AMRAD

ANDREA RADIO CORP.

Frank A. D. Andrea started FADA in 1918, building it up on amateur parts, then kits, then radio sets. He sold FADA in 1932, then rehired the key people when FADA went under in 1934. As Andrea Radio Corp. the company became a maker of premium-quality radio and television sets.

KT-E-5 TELEVISION KIT SOLD IN 1938
FOR $79.95. IS ALSO CHASSIS FOR 1-F-5

MODEL 1-F-5
17 TUBES 5" PICTURE ◊
1938

MODEL 8-F-12
"SHARP-FOCUS"
◊ TV-RADIO-PHONO
43 TUBES   12" PICTURE
1939

ANDREA RADIO CORP.

MODEL T-UI5
5 TUBES   AC-DC ◊
1947

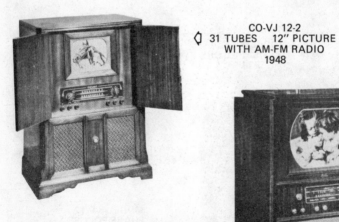

MODEL CO-UI5
◊ 5 TUBES   AC-DC
1947

MODEL P-163
5 TUBES   ALL-WAVE ◊
AC-DC-BATT
1947

CO-VJ 12-2
◊ 31 TUBES   12″ PICTURE
WITH AM-FM RADIO
1948

NORMANDY
19″ PICTURE WITH AM-FM ◊
1950

ARVIN
NOBLITT – SPARKS INDUSTRIES, INC.

RHYTHM SENIOR 527
5 TUBES $49.95
1936

RHYTHM MASTER 627
6 TUBES $69.95
1936

RHYTHM QUEEN 927
9 TUBES $99.50
1936

RHYTHM BABY 417
4 TUBES $19.95
1936

RHYTHM BELLE 467
4 TUBES $29.95
1936

RHYTHM KING 1127
11 TUBES $150.00
1936

RHYTHM JUNIOR 517
5 TUBES $34.95
1936

RHYTHM MAID 617
6 TUBES $59.95
1936

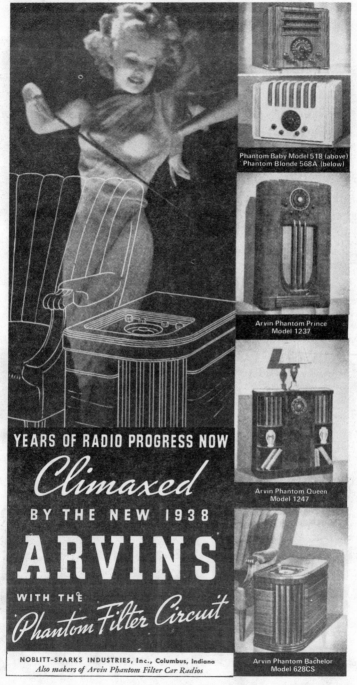

Phantom Baby Model 518 (above)
Phantom Blonde 568A (below)

Arvin Phantom Prince
Model 1237

Arvin Phantom Queen
Model 1247

Arvin Phantom Bachelor
Model 628CS

YEARS OF RADIO PROGRESS NOW

Climaxed

BY THE NEW 1938

ARVINS

WITH THE

Phantom Filter Circuit

NOBLITT-SPARKS INDUSTRIES, Inc., Columbus, Indiana
Also makers of Arvin Phantom Filter Car Radios

ARVIN

MODEL 58 AC-DC
$16.95 BLACK $19.95 IVORY
5 TUBES + BAL.   1938

MODEL 68
5 TUBES $24.95   1938

MODEL 78
5 TUBES $29.95   1938

MODEL 88 RADIO-PHONO
6 TUBES $39.95   1938

MODEL 40
CH. RE-49
2 TUBES   1940

MODEL 442
4 TUBES $12.95   1947

MODEL 524
CH. RE-100
5 TUBES   1942

240P BATT. PORT. $19.95
241P 3-WAY PORT. $29.95
4 TUBES   1949

360TFM FM-AM
6 TUBES $49.95   1949

Arvin

HOPALONG CASSIDY

Radio

William Boyd as Hopalong Cassidy, idol of millions of children!

Shatterproof!

$16⁹⁵

Designed to comply with Underwriters' requirements

MODEL 4080T
8½" PICTURE $129.50
1950

MODEL 2160 CM
16" PICTURE $249.95
1950

MODEL 440-T
$14.95   1950

A. Atwater Kent was a manufacturer of electrical parts for automobiles. He introduced a line of do-it-yourself "breadboard" radio components in 1921. He distributed his famous Model 5 as a sales promotion about the end of 1921, but concentrated on component kits until the fall of 1923. He introduced the Model 10 in time for Christmas 1923, followed by Model 9 and a broad line of breadboard sets. Today, the A-K breadboard is essential to any broad collection of early sets. Atwater Kent produced a line of fine radio sets until 1936, when he decided to shut his factory down because of rising costs and cheap competition.

ATWATER KENT
MFG. CO.

MODEL 57
METAL CABINET
7 TUBES $105.00
1929

MODEL 60
8 TUBES $80.00
1929

MODEL 60
IN KIEL TABLE
1929

MODEL 72
8 TUBES   1930

NATIONAL RECOVERY ACT,
1933.

63

ATWATER KENT

MODEL 2000
A-K 301N
◊ METAL CABINET
6 TUBES   1930

MODEL 521N
METAL CABINET ◊
7 TUBES   1930

MODEL 84
◊ GOLDEN VOICE
6 TUBES $69.50
1931

MODEL 558
8 TUBES   1933 ◊

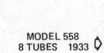

MODEL 93
◊ SHORT - WAVE ADAPTOR
4 TUBES   1933

64

ATWATER KENT

MODEL 310
10 TUBES   BC-SW
$89.00   1933

MODEL 510
10 TUBES   BC-SW
$99.00   1933

MODEL 711
11 TUBES   ALL-WAVE
$150.00   1933

MODEL 667
7 TUBES   BC-SW
1933

ATWATER KENT

MODEL 217
7 TUBES   BC-SW
$45.00   1933

MODEL 165
5 TUBES   BC-SW
$29.90   1933

MODEL 708
8 TUBES ALL-WAVE
$59.90   1933

MODEL 275
5 TUBES AC-DC
$29.90   1933

MODEL 206
6 TUBES 3 BANDS
$49.90   1934

MODEL 318K
8 TUBES   ALL-WAVE
$89.90   1934

MODEL 112N
12 TUBES   ALL-WAVE
$165.00   1934

MODEL 325E
5 TUBES   BL-SW
$49.90   1934

MODEL 145
5 TUBES   BL-SW
$39.90   1934

MODEL 944
4 TUBES $22.50
1934

69

AUTOMATIC RADIO MFG. CO.

Automatic Radio pioneered in auto radios, and also was probably the first East-coast maker of cathedral radios with the "Tom Thumb" compact model.

AUTOMATIC RADIO JR.
6 TUBES $49.50
1930

◊ AUTOMATIC RADIO SR.
"SG-224"
6 TUBES $95.00
1930

TOM THUMB MIDGET
6 TUBES $69.50 ◊
1930

P-72
◊ 3-IN-1 PORTABLE
5 TUBES $15.95
1939

3-IN-1- PORTABLE ◊
5 TUBES   1939

72

PORTABLE TELEVISION RECEIVER

STUNNING!
TELEVISION SET

Model 709

Featuring

7" Screen Brilliant Reproduction Full Channel Coverage
Horizontal Stabilizer   Vertical Stabilizer
Automatic Picture Lock
Clear FM Response Fine Tuning Rugged Construction
Hand-Rubbed Mahogany Cabinet

Television that's easy on the eye. Added sensitivity for faultless operation with brighter and steadier picture.

MODEL TV P490

All in a Single Unit
Good Looking
Wonderful Performance
Fine Tuning

★ **SIMPLE TO INSTALL!**

Antenna snaps into place and turns as necessary for excellent reception.

- Beautifully designed . . . new handsome Automatic Portable TV P490 in a rich tan leatherette cabinet.

- Show it in your customer's home and you're ready to show television at its best. Demonstrate how it can be easily moved from room to room . . . or at a summer home, camp, beach, etc.

- A demonstration is a sale. Make Big Profits now.

★ **PORTABLE!**

Total weight with antenna only 33 lbs.

SPECIAL ANNOUNCEMENT

Advance models of 10", 12½", 16" and Projection TV Models on display during the R.M.A. Show.

See us at Hotel Blackstone and Hotel Stevens—May 16-19

SINCE 1920

AUTOMATIC RADIO MFG. CO. INC.

122 BROOKLINE AVE., BOSTON 16, MASS.

CROSLEY CORP.

Powel Crosley, Jr. started making radios in 1921, and set up radio station WLW in 1922 to promote his products. Crosley pioneered the manufacture of good inexpensive sets, calling them the "Model T" of radio.

TRAVETTE
5 TUBES   1933 ◊

◊ COMPANION
5 TUBES   1933

MODEL 169 ◊
1934

THE FIVER
◊ 5 TUBES $19.99
1934

DUAL FIVER DELUXE ◊
5 TUBES   BC & SW
$29.95   1934

THE SIXTY-ONE
◊ 6 TUBES   BC & SW
$39.95   1934

MUSIC — GAYETY — ROMANCE — ENTERTAINMENT — SPORTS

only **$28⁹⁸** complete

CROSLEY

ROAMIO "4A1"

Self-contained as it is, the Crosley Roamio "4A1" can be easily installed in any car with the controls convenient to the driver, either to the right or left of steering wheel. The airplane type dial appears just below instrument panel.

WHATEVER HAPPENS... YOU'RE *THERE* WITH A CROSLEY

CROSLEY ROAMIO Unheard of value

THE CROSLEY RADIO CORPORATION   CINCINNATI   POWEL CROSLEY, Jr., President

76

CROSLEY CORP.

ROAMIO A-266
6 TUBES $39.95   1936
WITH TUNER HEAD.
BUILT-IN-SPEAKER

ROAMIO A-366
6 TUBES $54.95   1936
SEPARATE SPEAKER AND TUNER HEAD.
$64.95 WITH DUAL SPEAKERS

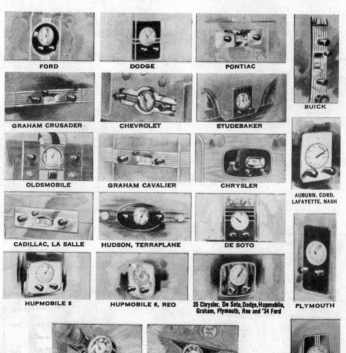

FORD

DODGE

PONTIAC

GRAHAM CRUSADER

CHEVROLET

STUDEBAKER

BUICK

OLDSMOBILE

GRAHAM CAVALIER

CHRYSLER

AUBURN, CORD,
LAFAYETTE, NASH

CADILLAC, LA SALLE

HUDSON, TERRAPLANE

DE SOTO

HUPMOBILE 8

HUPMOBILE 6, REO

35 Chrysler, De Soto, Dodge, Hupmobile,
Graham, Plymouth, Reo and '34 Ford

PLYMOUTH

STEERING COLUMN CONTROL
FOR ANY CAR

UNDER INSTRUMENT PANEL CONTROL
FOR ANY CAR

PACKARD

CROSLEY
CORPORATION

◊ MODEL 516
5 TUBES   1936

MODEL B-439A
BATTERY PORTABLE ◊
4 TUBES $18.95   1939

MODEL B-5549A
AC-DC-BATTERY
◊ SPRING-WOUND MOTOR
5 TUBES $39.95   1939

MODEL B-549A ◊
AC-DC-BATTERY
5 TUBES $79.95   1939

MODEL 66-T
◊ 6 TUBES   1946

MODEL 56PB
AC-DC-BATTERY ◊
5 TUBES   1946

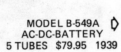

78

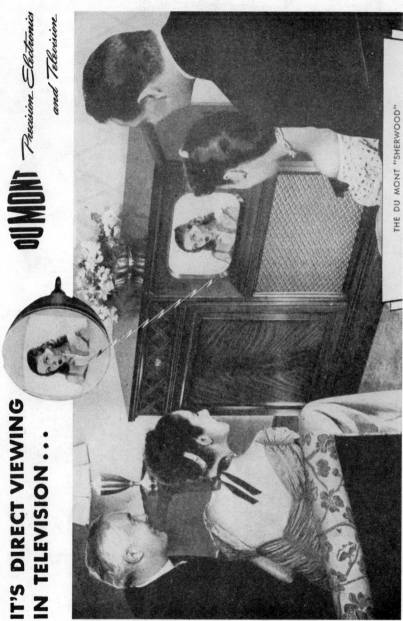

IT'S DIRECT VIEWING
IN TELEVISION...

RADIO AND TELEVISION RETAILING, AUGUST 1946

DU MONT *Precision Electronics and Television*

THE DU MONT "SHERWOOD"

EMERSON
RADIO & PHONOGRAPH CORP.

MICKEY MOUSE RADIO
4 TUBES   1933

 ◊ AC-DC UNIVERSAL COMPACT
4 TUBES $25.00
1933

MODEL U6D ◊
6 TUBES   1934

 ◊ MODEL U5A
5 TUBES   1935

MODEL U6F ◊
6 TUBES   1936

 ◊ MODEL BA199
4 TUBES + BALLAST
AC-DC   1938

EMERSON

AX SERIES
1938

MODEL 508
◊ 4 TUBE BATT.
1946

MODEL 541
5 TUBES   1946 ◊

MODEL 540
◊ "WORLD'S SMALLEST AC-DC
SUPERHET"   1947

MODEL 558
4 TUBES BATT. ◊
1948

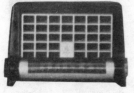

MODEL 636A
◊ 5 TUBES AC-DC
1950

EMERSON RADIO & PHONOGRAPH CORP.

MODEL 606
10" PICTURE
$349.50
1948

MODEL 608
16" PICTURE ◊
$599.50   1949

MODEL 609
◊ "PROTELGRAM" PROJECTION
SYSTEM, 20" SCREEN
$599.50   1949

MODEL 611
10" PICTURE   1949 ◊

The
FIRST THING
on
CHRISTMAS
MORNING

GENERAL ELECTRIC COMPANY

General Electric built radios since 1919, but sold them through RCA until 1930. G.E. was a major manufacturer, and entered the TV market in 1941.

THE STUDIO LOWBOY
7 TUBES   TRF
$112.50   1930

THE LOWBOY
9 TUBES   SUPERHET
$142.50   1930

THE HIGHBOY
9 TUBES   SUPERHET
$179.50   1930

MODEL S-22A
8 TUBES   1932
(BUILT BY RCA)

1931

RADIO

THE HIGHBOY—*(as illustrated)* 9-tube, Screen-Grid Super-Heterodyne, fitted with local-distant switch and tone control. Remote control available at additional cost. Brown walnut cabinet with French doors.
Less Radiotrons • Price **$179.50**

NEARLY one hundred million dollars is being spent on radio entertainment this year. By far the largest amount ever expended during one year on this form of home entertainment. Programs of unprecedented brilliance, world famous artists, the latest musical "hits", the voices of the great men and women of this and other countries, provide entertainment as never before.

TODAY'S FINE PROGRAMS DESERVE
GENERAL 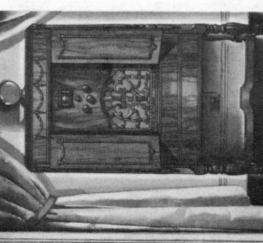 ELECTRIC

87

TWO LEADERS

MODEL K-40-A, 4-tube AC-DC receiver. (Handsome Walnut Case, surprising tone quality.) Easily portable, good performer. Dynamic speaker and voltage doubler improves reception greatly. (Shipped in standard package of four.) Price with tubes.......... **$1795**

MODEL L-50, table set. Five-tube superheterodyne, 110—125 volts, 25—133 cycles, AC, or DC. New tubes. Dynamic speaker. Additional switch for police calls. Good selectivity and sensitivity. Shipped in standard package of four. List price...... **$2475**

GENERAL ⟨GE⟩ ELECTRIC RADIO

GENERAL ELECTRIC

MODEL K-50
5 TUBES $24.95 ◊
1933

◊ MODEL K-60
"MANTEL CLOCK DESIGN"
6 TUBES $37.50
1933

MODEL K-64
BC-SW   1933 ◊
6 TUBES

MODEL K-63
◊ BC-SW   1933
6 TUBES

GENERAL ELECTRIC

MODEL K-85
ALL-WAVE
8 TUBES
1933

MODEL K-126
12 TUBES
1933

MODEL K-52
BC-SW
5 TUBES
1933

MODEL K-80
ALL-WAVE
8 TUBES
$92.50   1933

Auto Radio Trio

"We're in the Money"

Model B-52—G-E Portable Auto Radio. 5-tube superheterodyne that operates on car battery or 110-volt, 60-cycle A.C. Full, brilliant tone, particularly in higher registers. Low battery drain.

Model C-41—Four-tube set combining 7-tube performance with low battery drain. Brilliant tone even in high registers. Factory-sealed vibrator replaces rectifier tube. Ample volume.

Model C-61—G-E Deluxe Auto Radio. A 6-tube superheterodyne housed in a smartly designed case with highly polished metal grille. Remarkable performance at all car speeds. Greater volume—improved tone. Illuminated airplane-type dial.

The new GENERAL ⊕ ELECTRIC Auto Radio

91

GENERAL ELECTRIC

◊ MODEL F-53
5 TUBES   1937

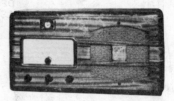

MODEL F-74 ◊
7 TUBES   1938

MODEL J-62 (MAHOGANY)
◊   J-620 (BLOND)
6 TUBES + BALLAST
1941

MODEL J-644 ◊
6 TUBES   1941

◊ MODEL H-77
7 TUBES   1939

MODEL H-116 ◊
11 TUBES   1939

GENERAL ELECTRIC

MODEL L-740
DE LUXE
$54.95   1941

F M CONVERTER
42-50MC
1941

MODEL 203
1946

MODEL 200
6 TUBES   AC-DC
1946

MODEL 250
5 TUBES   AC-BATT.
AIR CELL PLUS VIBRATOR
1946

MODEL 260
1947

G. E. MODEL 90 TV-AM-FM, 1939

SUPER-DISTANCE 801
10" PICTURE AM/TV
◊ 13 CHANNELS INCL CH.1
1948

SUPER-DISTANCE 901
PROJECTION TV, 3 SQ. FT.
TV/AM/FM/PHONO
13 CHANNELS INCL CH. 1   ◊
1948

Build up June gift sales!

WITH "WAKE-UP-TO-MUSIC" CLOCK-RADIOS

...erodyne G-E Clock-...ary plastic cabinet. Model 62. List price $41.95*.

G-E Clock-Radio—an extraordinary value. Rosewood plastic cabinet. Model 50. List price $29.95*.

Superheterodyne G-E Clock-Radio. Rosewood plastic cabinet. Model 60. List price $39.95*.

G-E Clock-Radio—beautiful design. Ivory plastic cabinet. Great value. Model 50W. List price $31.95*.

*Western prices slightly higher.
Prices subject to change without notice.

PORTABLES • TABLE MODELS • CONSOLES • FARM SETS • AUTOMATIC PHONOGRAPH COMBINATIONS • TELEVISION

95

THE HALLICRAFTERS CO.

MODEL T-54
19 TUBES + 4 RECT.
7" PICTURE
$169.50   1948 ◊

MODEL T-60
23 TUBES + 3 RECT.
16" x 20" PROJECTION SCREEN ◊
$595.00   1948

MODEL 505
19 TUBES + 4 RECT.
◊ $189.50   1948
(A slightly different
"Press Box" model was
offered early in 1948)

MODEL T-69
15" PICTURE
$259.50   1949
10" T-64 $179.50
12" T-64 $199.50   ◊
AVAILABLE IN VARIOUS
CONFIGURATIONS

THE INTERNATIONAL
KADETTE

TAKES ANOTHER BIG STEP FORWARD

The original Kadette was one of the biggest "hits" the radio industry has known. It galvanized sales. It piled up profits for thousands of dealers. Now, International—always a step ahead—announces its latest achievement. A new model—modern as the next minute—in design, features and performance.

In newness and sheer beauty of design, the new Kadette steps far ahead of traditional ideas. Contrasting planes of color — a fluted grille, finished in satin aluminum—unique illumination for dial and grille (on De Luxe model only) — all express a modern symmetry that establishes a new concept of fine appearance.

Although the Kadette is the world's smallest 5-tube super-heterodyne chassis, sensitivity, selectivity and tone quality have been immeasurably heightened. Operating only on 110 volts A.C. or D.C.—any cycle—the benefits of a.v.c.—tone control and superior quality is achieved.

Dealers—wire for details! Here's another radio sensation—a quality built product for quality minded people.

Originated and Manufactured by
INTERNATIONAL RADIO CORPORATION
ANN ARBOR, MICHIGAN

$25.00

COMPLETE WITH TUBES
DE LUXE MODEL $2.50 EXTRA

INTERNATIONAL RADIO CORP.

International Kadette (First volume-produced AC-DC set. First volume-produced plastic set) ◊ 4 tubes AC-DC. Introduced 1931, volume-production 1932, Home-Auto-Boat version 1933.

$12.50 Complete with tubes Deluxe Model $15

THE FIRST AND ONLY POCKET RADIO

KADETTE JR.
"WORLDS SMALLEST ◊
AC-DC RADIO"
$12.50 ($15.00 DELUXE)
1933

◊ KADETTE 87
7 TUBES
1936

KADETTE 36 ◊
6 TUBES
1937

JACKSON-BELL
CO. LTD.

JACKSON-BELL
"MADE BY GILFILLAN"
7 TUBES
1931 ◊

◊ MODEL 62 MODERN
6 TUBES
1933

JACKSON-BELL ◊
5 TUBES
1933

◊ PETER PAN
5 TUBES

MODEL 4 ◊
PETER PAN
1936

LINCOLN RADIO CORP.

MODEL 8-40
8 TUBES + 1 TUBE IN
8-40B POWER SUPPLY ◊
1930

◊ DELUXE 10 SUPER
10 TUBES
1930

DELUXE SW-31
10 TUBES 15-550M ◊
1931

◊ DELUXE SW-32
10 TUBES
1932

DELUXE SW-33
12 TUBES ◊
1932

THE MAGNAVOX COMPANY

Magnavox pioneered in advanced speaker designs since the early 1920's, moving into radio sets featuring single-dial tuning when others were still making three-dial radios. A quality house.

FIRST TRUE HIGH-
FIDELITY SYSTEM.
RADIO- PHONOGRAPH
1937

THE HEPPELWHITE
RADIO-PHONO
$145.00 ($198.50
WITH AUTOMATIC CHANGER)
1938

THE REGENT
RADIO-PHONO
$475.00   1938

THE IMPERIAL
RADIO-PHONO
1946

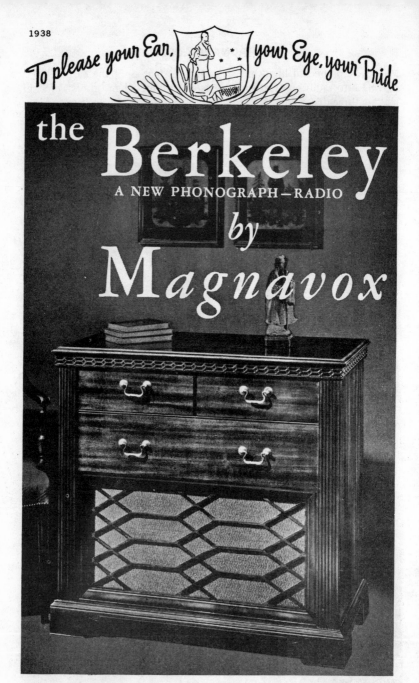

To please your Ear, your Eye, your Pride

the Berkeley
A NEW PHONOGRAPH—RADIO
by
Magnavox

The Oldest Name in Radio

MAJESTIC

"Majestic" was the trade name of Grigsby-Grunow Co., until it failed during the Depression in 1934. The Majestic Radio and Television Corporation carried on the Majestic name, and General Household Utilities carried on the Grunow name.

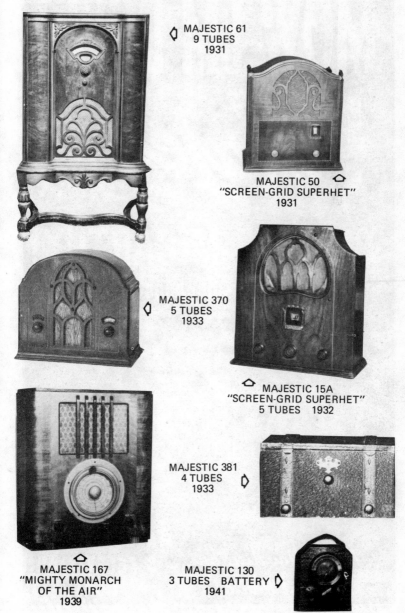

MAJESTIC 61
9 TUBES
1931

MAJESTIC 50
"SCREEN-GRID SUPERHET"
1931

MAJESTIC 370
5 TUBES
1933

MAJESTIC 15A
"SCREEN-GRID SUPERHET"
5 TUBES   1932

MAJESTIC 381
4 TUBES
1933

MAJESTIC 167
"MIGHTY MONARCH
OF THE AIR"
1939

MAJESTIC 130
3 TUBES   BATTERY
1941

107

MOTOROLA INC.
(GALVIN MFG. CORP.)

Paul Galvin made radio power supplies in 1928. In 1930 he introduced Motorola auto radios, and later became a major manufacturer. He then expanded into home radio products. Motorola developed the famous Handie-Talkie and Walkie-Talkie communications sets of World War II. Motorola also became a dominant manufacturer of mobile communications equipment. Motorola introduced its line of home television sets in 1947, and became one of the largest makers.

MOTOROLA'S FIRST
AUTO RADIO   PRODUCED ◊
1930

◊ TIME—TUNING
1938

⌂
LEADER
PUSH-BUTTON
6 TUBES $24.95
1939

◊ MODEL 61-CA
6 TUBES   1940

110

MOTOROLA, INC.

MOTOROLA INC.
(GALVIN MFG. CORP.)

MODEL 51D
THREE-POWER
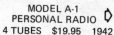 SUPERHETERODYNE
AC-DC-BATT
5 TUBES   1941

MODEL A-1 ◊
PERSONAL RADIO
4 TUBES $19.95   1942

VITA-TONE 101R21
◊ RADIO-PHONO-RECORDER
10 TUBES   1941

MODEL 51X19
5 TUBES   AC-DC ◊
1942

MODEL 5A5
◊ 5 TUBES   AC-DC-BATT
1946

MODEL 5L1U
4 TUBES + RECTIFIER ◊
AC-DC-BATT
1950

113

MOTOROLA, INC.
(GALVIN MFG. CORP. TO 1947)

MODEL VT-71
7" AC TUBE
FIRST SET BELOW $200.00
1947

MODEL VT-73
16 TUBES   7" PICTURE
1949

MODEL 10VT3
10" PICTURE 1949

MODEL 12VK 18
12" PICTURE   1949

Motorola

MODEL 20F1 . . . 20 inch
Rectangular tube. FM/AM
radio . . . 3-speed phono.
Limed Oak or Mahogany.

MODEL 17K1 . . .
17 inch picture tube.
Mahogany or Limed
Oak.

MODEL 17T3 . . . 17 inch
Rectangular tube. Plastic case. Value Price.

MODEL 17F4 . . . 17 inch
Rectangular tube. FM/AM
radio . . . 3-speed phono.
Rich Mahogany cabinet.

MOTOROLA Inc. CHICAGO

PHILCO BABY GRAND "CATHEDRAL" SETS

MODEL YEAR	MODEL NO.	TUBES	HEIGHT	QUANTITY MADE
1930	20B	7	17-5/8"	343,903
1931	70B	7	18"	288,620
"	90B	9	18-9/16"	106,050
1932	51B	5		23,800
"	52B	5	16-1/8"	28,420
"	71B	7	18-3/16"	44,700
"	80B	4	13-11/16"	196,175
1933	60B	5	16-1/4"	89,300
"	89B	6	16"	94,390
"	19B	6	16-13/16"	20,750
"	14B	9	18-1/2"	13,000
"	17B	11	18-13/16"	2,350
"	16B	11	19-7/16"	22,100
1934	84B	4	14-1/8"	28,980
"	60B	5	16-3/16"	178,500
"	44B	6	18-7/16"	10,000
"	89B	6	16-9/16"	58,575
"	118B	8	18-3/4"	19,198
"	144B	6	19-5/8"	16,070
1935	84B	4	14-1/4"	75,200
1936	60B	5	16-13/16"	55,216
"	89B	6	16-3/16"	7,000
"	84B/33B	4/?	14-1/2"	113,600
"	60B	5	17"	102,200
	620B/ 623B/ 624B	6		50,000
1937	93B		14-1/2"	5,300
1938	70B			35,635
			BABY GRAND TOTAL	2,029,032

We thank William E. Denk for assembling the Philco information.

PHILCO CORP.

Philco Corporation began in 1892 as Helios Electric Co., and became the Philadelphia Storage Battery Co. in 1906. A maker of batteries and power supplies, Philco jumped into A-C radios in 1927 and became a tremendous success as one of the "big three" radio manufacturers along with RCA and Zenith. Early Philco is best remembered for the "Baby Grand" line, designed for the depression years. These sets are now known as cathedral, compact or gothic models. Philco had a broad line of consumer radio products, and was among the first to introduce a line of television sets.

Note that there were often several versions and year models of the same type numbers. Earlier cathedral models (e.g. 20B, 79B, 80B, 90B) were powerful console-type chasses in table cabinets, while later models (e.g. 80B, 84B) employed smaller chasses.

MODEL 20B
7 TUBES   TRF $49.50 NEW ◊
1930

MODEL 70B
◊ 7 TUBES SUPERHET $49.95
1931

MODEL 90B
9 TUBES   SUPERHET ◊
$69.50   1931

MODEL 51B
◊ 5 TUBES   SUPERHET
$39.50   1932

117

PHILCO CORP.

MODEL 80B
4 TUBES
◊ REGENERATIVE SUPERHET
1932

MODEL 60B
5 TUBES $29.50 ◊
1933

MODEL 16B
◊ 11 TUBES SUPERHET $89.50
1933

MODEL 81B
4 TUBES REGEN. SUPER. ◊
1933

PHILCO CORP.

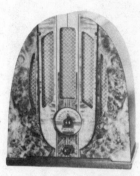

MODEL 60B
5 TUBES
1934

MODEL 84B
4 TUBES REGEN. SUPER.
$20.00   1934

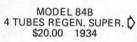

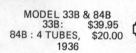

MODEL 89B
6 TUBES
1934

MODEL 33B & 84B
33B: $39.95
84B : 4 TUBES, $20.00
1936

MODEL 116B
10 TUBES   1936

119

PHILCO CORP.

MODEL 620B/623B/624B
AC/BATT/6VDC
$52.50/65.00/75.00
6 TUBES   1936 ▷

◁ MODEL 93B
$22.95
1937

MODEL 70B ▷
$24.45
1938

MODEL 65 "THE CONSOLE"
◁ 6 TUBES $102.00
EARLY SCREEN GRID
(METAL VERSION MADE 1929)
45,000 MADE
1930

PHILCO CORP.

MODEL 96H HIGHBOY
9 TUBES $145.00   ◊
43,098 MADE
1930

MODEL 70L
◊ 7 TUBES $59.17
49,000
1931

MODEL 90-H HIGHBOY
9 TUBES $109.75   ◊
20,890
1931

MODEL 112L LOWBOY
◊ (NORMAN BEL GEDDES CABINET DESIGN)
11 TUBES $149.50
28,857
1931

PHILCO CORP.

MODEL 52L
LOWBOY
5 TUBES $89.17
(22 GUINEAS ENGLISH)
13,196 MADE
1932

MODEL 70
GRANDFATHER'S
CLOCK
7 TUBES
$89.50
8,000
1932

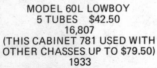

MODEL 60L LOWBOY
5 TUBES $42.50
16,807
(THIS CABINET 781 USED WITH
OTHER CHASSES UP TO $79.50)
1933

MODEL 91X
9 TUBES   3,600
1933

122

PHILCO CORP.

MODEL 57C
4 TUBES $22.50
110,500 MADE
1933

MODEL 45 & 28C
6 TUBES $49.95
58,300   1934

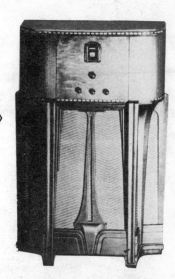

MODEL 200X
10 TUBES   1934

MODEL 507L
RADIO-PHONO
8 TUBES   1934

123

PHILCO CORP.

◊ MODEL 116
10 TUBES   1935

MODEL 604C ◊
5 TUBES   1936

◊ TRANSITONE 610T
ALL-WAVE
5 TUBES   1936

TRANSITONE 7T
5 TUBES BATT'Y. ◊
1937

◊ TRANSITONE 10T
6 TUBES   1937

MODEL 37-690X
HIGH-FIDELITY WITH
AUTOMATIC TUNING
20 TUBES, 3 SPEAKERS, ACCOUSTIC
CHAMBERS, ALL-WAVE, BAND-SPREAD
$395.00
1937

MODEL 15DX
11 TUBES
1937

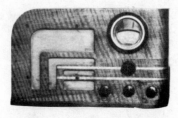

MODEL 6C
1938

TRANSITONE 30T
ALL-WAVE
1938

MODEL 38-9
6 TUBES
1938

PHILCO CORP.

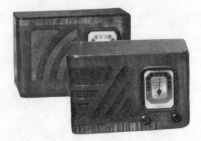

MODEL 38-12
◁ 5 TUBES   AC-DC
1938

PHILCO PAL
FIRST PHILCO PORTABLE ◊
INTRO. 1938
1939 MODEL YEAR

TRANSITONE PT-27,28
◊ (27 OUTSIDE ANT., 28 LOOP ANT.)
5 TUBES   AC-DC
1939

MODEL 39-6760
5 TUBES   ◊
AC-DC-BATT
1939

TRANSITONE PT-25,26
◁ (25 OUTSIDE ANT., 26 LOOP ANT.)
5 TUBES   AC-DC
1940

TRANSITONE PT-88
5 TUBES AC-DC-BATT ◊
1939

PHILCO CORP.

MODEL 116RX-SU (39-116)
ALL-WAVE WITH "MYSTERY CONTROL"
13 TUBES + 1 TUBE REMOTE
CONTROL UNIT.
1939

MODEL 40-90
4 TUBES BATTERY ◊
1940

MODEL 40-150 ◊
8 TUBES   1940

MODEL 40-200 ◊
11 TUBES
1940

127

AUTO RADIOS FOR 1941

Control Plates to Match the Panels of ALL Cars ...AT NO EXTRA COST!

Philco offers you for 1941 an extremely simple and flexible control plate proposition. The controls for all models are exactly the same size and shape.

Speakers to Mount in Grilles of All Cars

New! Exclusive! Short-Wave Tuner

A brand-new accessory, invented by Philco engineers, that makes a short-wave radio out of any 1941 Philco Auto Radio (except AR-10)! Adds two tubes and four short-waves users to enjoy rare reception. Tops too far Short-Wave in spots on grams noisy for good reception or too standard bands. A sensation. *Only Philco has it!* Only . . . PLUS for Philco dealers. **$20**

AR-45. Two-unit Superheterodyne in a beautifully finished Tan Case with Yellow Ornament. 6 tubes. Choice of separate 7-inch Grille Speaker or Under-Dash Speaker. Separate Control Unit with 2-point Tone Control, Illuminated Dial and Plate to match any car. **$34⁹⁵**

AR-75. De Luxe two-unit Superheterodyne with 8 tubes. Separate 8-inch Under-Dash Speaker. Both set and speaker finished in refreshing Ludington Green with Chrome Trim. R. F. Stage Push-Pull Beam Output. Separate Illuminated Control Unit with Single Push-Button for 5 favorite stations, 3-point Tone Control and Plate to match any car. **$59⁹⁵**

AR-40. Single-unit Superheterodyne in a smart new case finished in Tan. 6 tubes, powerful Built-in 6-inch Speaker. Separate Control Unit with 2-point Tone Control, Illuminated Dial and Plate to match any car. Fine all-around performance. A big value. **$29⁹⁵**

AR-55. Two-unit Superheterodyne in Crystal Green Case with Yellow Ornament. 6 tubes. Choice of separate 7-inch Grille Speaker or Under-Dash Speaker. Separate Illuminated Control Unit—left knob controls volume and tone, right knob tunes all stations or acts as push-button; for 5 favorite stations as push-button. **$44⁹⁵** Superb tone and performance.

AR-10. Attractive, rugged one-piece case finished in beautiful Crystal Green. Fits snugly under the instrument panel of any car. 6-tube Superheterodyne with Built-in Speaker and Illuminated, Easy-to-read Dial. The finest low-priced auto radio ever offered . . . **$19⁹⁵**

AR-50. Single-unit Superheterodyne in the new Crystal Green Case with Chrome Trim. 6 tubes. Powerful Built-in 6-inch Speaker. Separate Illuminated Control Unit with new tuning convenience—left knob controls volume and tone, right knob tunes all stations or acts as push-button for 5 favorite stations. Plate to **$39⁹⁵** match any car. Only . . . . .

Today, the great majority of radios operating in the cars of America have been manufactured by Philco. **PHILCO ALL YEAR 'ROUND**

PHILCO CORP.

MODEL 255T
(ALSO 41-255)
9 TUBES
1940

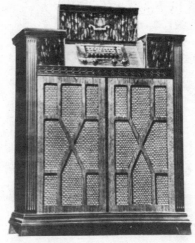

MODEL 287X
(ALSO 41-287)
9 TUBES
1941

MODEL 603P
(ALSO 41-603)
6 TUBES
1940

MODEL 607P
(ALSO 41-607)
6 TUBES
1940

129

PHILCO CORP.

MODEL 380X
(SEE ALSO 42-380, 1942) ◊
AM-SW
8 TUBES
1941

◊ MODEL 395X
(ALSO 42-395)
AM-FM-SW
9 TUBES
1941

MODEL 1003
(ALSO 42-1003)
◊ AM-SW-PHONO
7 TUBES   1941

MODEL 1005
(ALSO 42-1005)
BC-SW-PHONO ◊
7 TUBES
1941

PHILCO CORP.

TRANSITONE PT-87
(ALSO 42-PT87)
5 TUBES   1941

TRANSITONE PT-88
(ALSO 42-PT88)
5 TUBES   1941

TRANSITONE PT-91
(ALSO 42-PT91)
5 TUBES   1941

MODEL 323T
(ALSO 42-323)
6 TUBES   1941

MODEL 355T
(ALSO 42-355)
AM-FM-SW
8 TUBES   1941

132

PHILCO CORP.

MODEL 3710
REFRIGERATOR-TOP ◊
CLOCK-RADIO
1941

TRANSITONE PT-26
◊ WARTIME MATERIALS VERSION:
SEE EARLIER PT-26
5 TUBES   1941

MODEL 41-226 ◊
6 TUBES
1941

◊ MODEL 41-230
7 TUBES
1941

MODEL 41-608
RADIO-PHONO-RECORDER ◊
9 TUBES
1941

PHILCO CORP.

MODEL 1015
(ALSO 42-1015)
AM-FM-SW-PHONO ◊
12 TUBES
1941

MODEL 42-380
◊ (NOTE SLIGHT DIFFERENCE FROM 380X)
AM-SW   8 TUBES
1942

MODEL 42-321 ◊
1942

◊ MODEL 42-350
7 TUBES
1942

TRANSITONE PT-95 ◊
5 TUBES
1942

PHILCO CORP.

MODEL 47-205
5 TUBES   AC-DC
1947

MODEL 46-1217
1946 ◊

MODEL 48-1264
AM-FM-PHONO
9 TUBES   1947

MODEL 48-1266
AM-FM-PHONO
9 TUBES   1947

MODEL 48-206
1948

MODEL 48-485
6 TUBES   AC-DC ◊
1948

PHILCO CORP.

MODEL 48-1286
◊ AM-FM-PHONO
11 TUBES   1948

MODEL 48-1290
AM-FM-PHONO ◊
13 TUBES   1948

49-1604
◊ AM-RADIO-PHONO
6 TUBES   AC-DC
1949

138

PHILCO CORP.

MODEL 48-1000
PHILCO'S FIRST ▷
1948

MODEL 49-1002
◁ $324.50   7,012 MADE
1949

MODEL 50-702
$189.50   8,950 ▷
1949

MODEL 50-1104
◁ $229.95   26,095
1949

PHILCO CORP.

49-101
4 TUBES + RECT. ◊
AC-DC
1949

◊ 49-501
5 TUBES   AC-DC
1949

49-505
5 TUBES   AC-DC ◊
1949

◊ 49-601
AC-DC-BATT
1949

49-901
5 TUBES   AC-DC ◊
1948-49

◊ 49-1401
AM RADIO-PHONO
5 TUBES   AC-DC
1949

PHILCO CORP.

MODEL 50-501
UNIVERSAL
◊ 5 TUBES + RECT.
1950

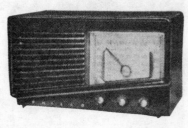

MODEL 50-925
AM-FM ◊
6 TUBES 1950

MODEL 50-1420
◊ RADIO-PHONO
5 TUBES 1950

MODEL 50-1727
AM-FM-PHONO ◊
11 TUBES 1950

MODEL 51-537
◊ CLOCK-RADIO
5 TUBES AC-DC
1950

TRAFFIC!

the most sensational store traffic builder since Television began!

PILOT *Candid T-V*

to retail at

99⁵⁰

Plus $1.55 Fed. Tax

with Extra Sensitivity for Fine Reception Even in Hard-To-Get Fringe Areas

WANT MORE BUSINESS? GET more business with the most amazing drawing-card in television history—PILOT CANDID T-V! A nation-wide runaway seller...the ONLY SUPERB T-V set under $100! A fine portable precision instrument with powerful 17-tube chassis (plus 3 rectifiers and personal-sized 3″ cathode ray tube). PILOT CANDID T-V is a sure winner . . . cash in on this great seller NOW!

Remember these other Great PILOT TRAFFIC BUILDERS ?

1927 the first short-wave home receiver

1937 the first truly portable battery set

1947 the first popular-priced FM tuner (Pilotuner)

MAIL COUPON FOR DETAILS TODAY!

Pilot Radio Corp.
37-06 36th Street, Long Island City, N. Y.

Please send me full details about the amazing new PILOT CANDID T-V:

Name

Address

City_____ Zone_____ State_____

PILOT RADIO CORPORATION, 37-06 36th STREET, LONG ISLAND CITY, N. Y.

Other fine Pilot Television Sets from $99.50 to $1195

143

RADIO CORPORATION OF AMERICA

DAVID SARNOFF

RCA was first formed to solve a problem. United States wireless communications prior to and during World War I were owned by foreign interests, particularly the Marconi Wireless Telegraph Company of America, a British based operation. The U. S. government intervened, and RCA was formed on October 17, 1919. On November 20, RCA acquired the "American Marconi" operation and business commenced December 1. General Electric and Westinghouse built sets only for sale by RCA under the original government pact, and continued to do so until 1930. Ed J. Nally of American Marconi was the first president of RCA, and put the new company into operation. He was followed as president by David Sarnoff, a man of remarkable imagination, drive and business ability. While with American Marconi in 1916, Sarnoff envisioned the great possibilities of radio broadcasting. He not only went on to build RCA into the greatest of the radio broadcast and radio set builders, he also formed the National Broadcasting Company as a new RCA operation in 1926. RCA pioneered in practical television, and developed the remarkable compatible color television system which won acceptance after a long, hard struggle. RCA was a major factor in World War II military communications and electronic equipment, based on long commercial and technical experience. RCA's great productivity in developing and manufacturing vacuum tubes was a major factor in developing the entire radio-electronics industry. RCA sold $586,393,000 in goods and services in 1950, and had about 55,000 employees at year-end.

RCA ARCHIVES, 1951

RCA Victor — World Leader in Radio . . . First in Television

145

RCA

During the 1930-1950 period most sets were produced by the Victor Division of RCA, as the RCA Victor. Most sets were the superior "Superheterodynes," for which RCA controlled the patents.

◊ **MODEL R-39**
"MICRO-SYNCHRO RADIO"
8 TUBES   1930

MODEL 48
SCREEN-GRID TRF ◊
7 TUBES $112.50
1930

RADIOLA 86
◊ **RADIO-PHONO-RECORDER**
9 TUBES   1930

MODEL P-31
PORTABLE ◊
8 TUBES   1932

Meet my new family

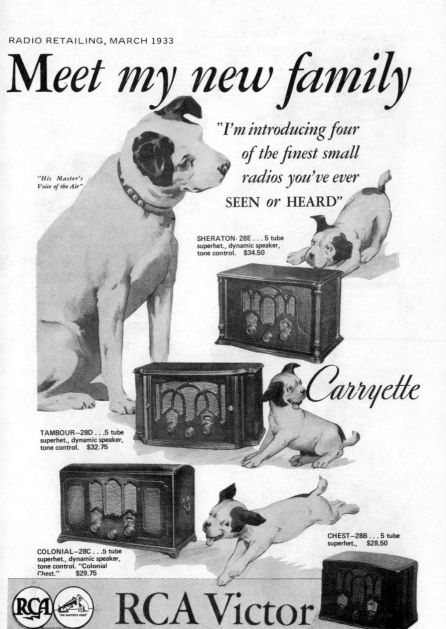

"I'm introducing four
of the finest small
radios you've ever
SEEN or HEARD"

"His Master's
Voice of the Air"

SHERATON- 28E . . . 5 tube
superhet., dynamic speaker,
tone control. $34.50

Carryette

TAMBOUR—28D . . .5 tube
superhet., dynamic speaker,
tone control. $32.75

COLONIAL—28C . . .5 tube
superhet., dynamic speaker,
tone control. "Colonial
Chest." $29.75

CHEST—28B . . .5 tube
superhet., $28.50

RCA   RCA Victor

RCA

MODEL R-22S
◊ 5 TUBES   AC-DC
$24.75   1933

MODEL 28 CARRYETTE
5 TUBES   4 CONTROLS ◊
1933

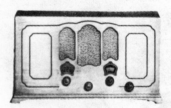

MODEL R-28 CARRYETTE
◊ 5 TUBES   4 CONTROLS
1933

MODEL R-28B CARRYETTE ◊
5 TUBES   4 CONTROLS
$24.95   1933

MODEL 143
◊ 8 TUBES   1933

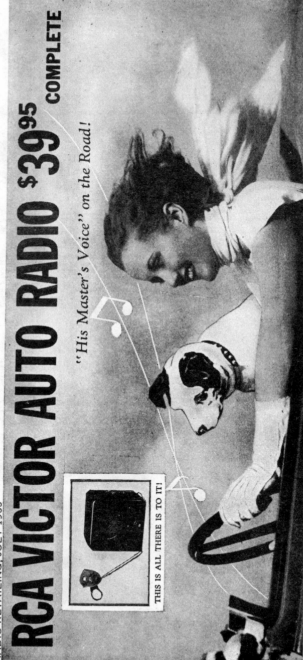

RCA VICTOR AUTO RADIO $39⁹⁵ COMPLETE

"His Master's Voice" on the Road!

THIS IS ALL THERE IS TO IT!

Now hear thrilling Police calls!

Model R-28

Model R-38

R-28 $19.95
R-37 $29.95
R-38 $49.95
RE-40 $49.95

Model RE-40

Model R-37

RCA Victor Radio Sets

150

RCA

MODEL 310
"DUO" RADIO-PHONO
5 TUBES   TRF ◊
1934

MODEL 340
◊ "ALL WAVE DUO"
RADIO-PHONO
8 TUBES   1934

MODEL C-13-2
13 TUBES, 140KC-60MC ◊
1935

◊ MODEL 7T
7 TUBES   1936

151

RCA

MODEL 5T
5 TUBES   1936 ◊

MODEL 9K-2
◊ MAGIC VOICE, MAGIC BRAIN,
MAGIC EYE, METAL TUBES
9 TUBES   ALL-WAVE
$129.95   1936

MODEL 5X
5 TUBES   AC-DC $32.95 ◊
1936

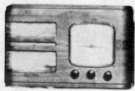

◊ MODEL 85T
5 TUBES   1936

MODEL 10T
ALL-WAVE
10 TUBES, 140KC-60MC ◊
1937

152

RCA

MODEL 7K1
6 TUBES   1937

MODEL 810K1
9 TUBES   1938

MODEL 95T5
5 TUBES   1938

MODEL 96T1
6 TUBES   1938

MODEL 5Q55
5 TUBES $29.95
1939

9TX-31 LITTLE NIPPER
5 TUBES $9.95
1939

153

RCA

TT-5 TELEVISION ATTACHMENTS
17 TUBES, 5" PICTURE, 5 CHANNELS

(Played through home radio speaker. Most
sets had dial plate on channel knob, marked
6-5-4-3-2)

1939

MODEL TRK-12
37 TUBES,   12" PICTURE ◊
1939

◊ MODEL TRK-9
9" PICTURE   1939

154

RCA

MODEL 45X1
5 TUBES   1940

MODEL 45X11
5 TUBES   1940

MODEL 45X13
5 TUBES   1940

MODEL 110K
10 TUBES   BC-SW
1940

MODEL 19
9 TUBES   1940

MODEL 46X11
5 TUBES   1940

MODEL 46X13
5 TUBES   1940

MODEL T-62
6 TUBES   1940

155

RCA VICTOR VALUE— THESE NEW LEADERS

★ **RCA VICTOR Super-Eight (Model 28X)**—Super-tone with 9¼" Ellipticon Speaker . . . 8 RCA Victor Preferred Type Tubes . . . Overseas Dial with Spread-band tuning . . . American and foreign reception . . . 2 built-in antennas . . . AC-DC operation.

★ **RCA VICTOR De Luxe Super-Eight (Model 28X-5)**—This super-set is packed with super-features that will thrill your customers. Embodies all the features of the Super-Eight plus Automatic Electric Tuning (5 stations) . . . AC-DC operation.

★ **RCA VICTOR Model 28T**
A winner in any company! 8 RCA Victor Preferred Type Tubes . . . 9¼" Ellipticon Speaker . . . 3-band Overseas Dial with Spread-band tuning . . . Electric Tuning (6 stations) . . . 2 built-in antennas . . . and many other features.

★ **RCA VICTOR Model 26X-3**
Its superb features and sensational low price will bring you many orders. 6 RCA Victor Preferred Type Tubes, providing 8-tube performance . . . 2-band Overseas Dial with Spread-band tuning . . . AC-DC operation, and many others.

★ **RCA VICTOR Model 26X-4**
Here's a set that will virtually sell itself! 6 RCA Victor Preferred Type Tubes (8-tube performance)...2-band Overseas Dial with Spread-band tuning...Electric Tuning (5 stations) . . . 2 built-in antennas . . . AC-DC.

★ **RCA VICTOR Model 26X-1**
Packs a sales wallop with 6 RCA Victor Preferred Type Tubes (8-tube performance) . . . 2-band Overseas Dial with Spread-band tuning . . . American and improved foreign reception . . . built-in Magic Loop antenna . . . AC-DC.

★★★ SUMMER SPECIALS WITH SALES-SOCK! ★★★

★ **RCA Victor Personal Radio Model BP-10 with Carrying Case**
a $26.50 value your customers will go for at $20! Genuine leather carrying case free with purchase of easy-to-carry radio which weighs only 4¼ lbs. Has four RCA Victor Tynetron Tubes (6-tube performance) . . . Ellipticon Speaker . . . built-in antenna.

★ **RCA Victor Three-Way "Pick-Me-Up" Model 25BP**
is a splendid all-purpose set. Operates on batteries or AC-DC . . . 5 RCA Victor Preferred Type Tubes . . . Permanent magnet dynamic speaker . . . built-in Magic Loop antenna . . . easy-reading, clock type dial . . . finished in durable, two-tone tan leatherette.

RCA

MODEL BP-10
◊ 4 TUBES   BATT'Y
1941

MODEL 2X61
6 TUBES   AC-DC ◊
1941

MODEL 94BP1
◊ 4 TUBES BATT'Y   1941

25BT-2 ELECTRIFIER ◊
BATTERY   1942

MODEL 55X
◊ 5 TUBES   1942

GLOBE TROTTER
(FIRST OF A SERIES) ◊
AC-DC-BATT   1946

MODEL 65U
◊ "GOLDEN THROAT"
RADIO-PHONO
5 TUBES   1947

RCA

MODEL 66X2
6 TUBES   AM-SW
1948

MODEL 65X1 ◊
5 TUBES   1948 ◊

◊ MODEL 66X13
6 TUBES   AM-SW
1948

MODEL 68R1
8 TUBES   AM-FM ◊
1948

◊ MODEL 75X1
5 TUBES   1948

MODEL 77U
AM-PHONO
6 TUBES + RECT. ◊
1948

RCA 630TS
THE FAMOUS BASIC CIRCUIT
FOLLOWED BY MOST
MANUFACTURERS. FIRST MASS-
PRODUCED TELEVISION SET.
10" PICTURE $350.00
1946

 MODEL 8TS30
1948

MODEL 9TW333 ◊
TV-AM-FM-PHONO
1949

159

Greater Variety for Greater Sales!

... you can offer your customers the new RCA Victor system in their choice of 7 magnificent instruments ... all (except the attachment, of course) with the exclusive RCA Victor "Golden Throat" tone system.

Model 9TW333—52-square-inch RCA Victor Eye Witness Television, FM-AM radio, 78 rpm automatic changer for 10- and 12-inch records, *plus* the new RCA Victor system of recorded music. Walnut, mahogany or blond finished cabinet with generous storage space for 7-inch records.

Model 9EY3—Smartly styled, compact RCA Victor Player in a rich maroon plastic cabinet with distinctive, gold-colored trim. Here is a complete phonograph to offer your customers the advantages of this new system at an amazingly low price.

Model 9W105—A console with AM and static-free FM radio with a powerful 12-inch speaker ... 78 rpm record changer *plus* the new RCA Victor system of recorded music. Mahogany, walnut or blond finished cabinet has ample storage for records ... 7-, 10- and 12-inch.

Model 9W101—Superb FM-AM radio ... and the new RCA Victor system of recorded music. Rich traditional cabinet of attractive walnut or lovely mahogany finish. Storage for 216 singles or 24 albums ... more than 38 hours of this great new listening pleasure.

Model 9JY—Easily attached to any make set, this fully automatic new RCA Victor Player brings your customers the new distortion-free recordings—50-minute programs without need of attention—at a new low price!

Model 9W103 — FM and AM radio, a big 12-inch speaker, plus the exciting new RCA Victor system of recorded music. Beautifully finished in limed oak, walnut, or mahogany, the cabinet stores 33 hours of recorded music—189 singles or 24 of the new albums.

Model 9Y7—The most amazing table combination ever offered. Imagine ... an automatic record changer ... powerful Standard Band radio plus storage space for as many as 60 playing sides—all in one compact table model. Finished in walnut, mahogany or blond.

The new RCA Victor system is the modern, inexpensive way to enjoy recorded music. It offers more advantages and enjoyment than does any other type of record or record playing equipment. The advantages start with low cost and run a course of conveniences never before heard of. The enjoyment starts with a distortion-free record and continues with exactly the music your customers want when they want it. This combination of advantages and enjoyment has been calculated to best suit the desires of the greatest number of your customers.

RCA VICTOR

DIVISION OF RADIO CORPORATION OF AMERICA

RCA

 MODEL RC1046A/B274
6 TUBES   1948

MODEL BX6
GLOBE TROTTER
5 TUBES + RECT.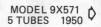
AC-DC-BATT
1950

 MODEL 551 (BLACK)
MODEL 552 (IVORY)
CHASSIS 1089
5 TUBES   AC-DC
1950

MODEL 9X571 ◊
5 TUBES   1950

◊ MODEL 9X561
5 TUBES   1950

MODEL A78 ◊
AM-FM-PHONO
7 TUBES   1950

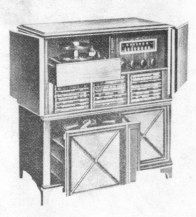

RCA

MODEL 641
◊ AM-FM-PHONO-TV
1949

MODEL TC-165
16" PICTURE $349.50 ◊
1949

MODEL T 164
◊ 16" PICTURE
BUILT-IN ANTENNA
1950

MODEL T 120
12½" PICTURE
BUILT-IN ANTENNA ◊
(10" T100 ALSO AVAILABLE)
1950

MODEL S 1000
TV-AM-FM-SW-PHONO
16'' PICTURE   1950

MODEL TA 128
TV-AM-FM-PHONO
12½'' PICTURE   1950

MODEL TA 129
TV-AM-FM-PHONO
12½'' PICTURE   1950

MODEL TA 169
TV-AM-FM-PHONO
16'' PICTURE   1950

MODEL TC 165
16'' PICTURE
1950

MODEL TC 167
16'' PICTURE
1950

"HIS MASTER'S VOICE"...

"Hello! Lots of people don't know it but my name is NIPPER. I was a real dog who really recognized 'His Master's Voice' back in 1898."

"And then I had to do the hardest work of my life—*posing!* If there's one thing I don't like to do, it's to sit still . . . But I did it for hours!"

"Then they took Mr. Barraud's painting of me and ran it as a Victrola* advertisement . . . I was started on my career to world fame!"

"Next, another kind of 'music box' came along—a radio made by RCA. Then when RCA merged with Victor—in 1929, I became *even more famous!*"

*"Victrola"—T.M. Reg. U.S. Pat. Off.

 RCA VICTOR

the history of a famous Trade Mark

INTERESTING SETS

COLONIAL
"NEW WORLD"
◊ 2—BAND SUPERHET
5 TUBES AC-DC
$59.50   1933

COLONIAL
"CLOCK CABINET" ◊
1931

FADA
MODEL KG ◊
7 TUBES   1931

GENERAL MOTORS CORP.
◊ "REMOTE CONTROL UNIT"
1932

GLOBE RADIO
"CHAIRSIDE" ◊
1930 EST.

E. H. SCOTT

SCOTT RADIO LABORATORIES

NOW... *a Radio*

GUARANTEEING
WORLD-WIDE RECEPTION

new
15-550 METER
SCOTT
ALL-WAVE
Deluxe

1932

WORLD-WIDE
RECEPTION
LONG A
GUARANTEED
ACTUALITY

with
THIS RADIO!   **SCOTT ALLWAVE DELUXE**
15-550 Meter Superheterodyne
1934

GO
GLOBE-TROTTING
AT HOME
with a

Custom-built
SCOTT   ALL-WAVE FIFTEEN
1934

As the Map of Europe
CHANGES DAY BY DAY

Get the TRUE PICTURE
with the
WORLD'S MOST
POWERFUL
RADIO

USED IN 154 COUNTRIES FOR ITS
AMAZING LONG DISTANCE RECEPTION!
1939

THE STRADIVARIUS
SCOTT
OF RADIO RECEIVERS

SCOTT RADIO LABORATORIES, INC.

1940 AM-FM CHASSIS

E. H. Scott's Scott Transformer Co. introduced a top-quality all-wave receiver in 1928. This grew into the Scott Radio Laboratories' line of very expensive, beautifully-designed, chrome-plated chasses. Scott's cabinets were exquisite pieces of workmanship, but many of the chasses were sold as showpieces without cabinets. Scott's was the "Cord-Auburn-Duesenberg" line of the radio world. Scott made sets through the 1930's and 1940's, culminating in a line of high-quality television sets in 1949. E. H. Scott himself left the company in 1945.

SCOTT ALL-WAVE

"THE STRADIVARIUS
OF RADIO RECEIVERS"

167

SOME OF THE OTHER FACES OF SCOTT

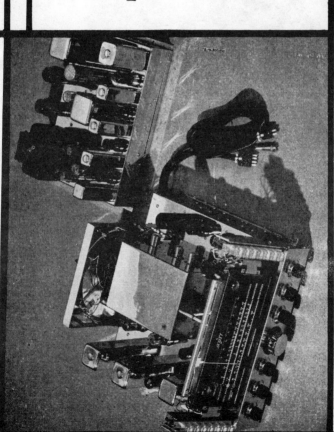
169

SCOTT RADIO LABORATORIES, INC.

SCOTT CHIPPENDALE
◊ AM-FM-PHONO ALL—WAVE
1946

MODEL 800BT
WITH PROTELGRAM PROJECTION ◊
AM-FM-PHONO ALL-WAVE
16″ x 12″ SCREEN
$1975.00   1949

MODEL 400 A
◊ WITH PROTELGRAM PROJECTION
16″ x 12″ SCREEN
$695.00 PLUS TABLE
1949

SILVERTONE
SEARS, ROEBUCK & CO.

◊ MODEL F
5 TUBES   1933

MODEL R 7459
12 TUBES   1933 EST. ◊

◊ MODEL 1650
8 TUBES   1935

MODEL ALL-WAVE ◊
9 TUBES $39.95
1936

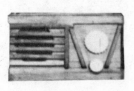

◊ MODEL 109.199-1
5 TUBES   1940

SILVERTONE
SEARS, ROEBUCK & CO.

MODEL 6437
12 TUBES   ALL-WAVE
1940

MODEL 6050
CHASSIS 132.825-2
4 TUBES   1941

MODEL 8005
CH. 132-839.1
5 TUBES   1948

MODEL 7070
7 TUBES   1942

MODEL 132.818
4 TUBES   AC-DC
1946
(ARVIN)

SILVERTONE
SEARS, ROEBUCK & CO.

MODEL 101.808
6 TUBES   AC-DC
1949

MODEL 101.822A
6 TUBES
AC-DC-BATT
1949

MODEL 132.857
5 TUBES   1950

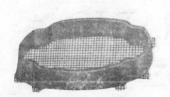

TYPICAL 1950 SILVERTONE AUTO RADIO KIT

173

SPARTON RADIO
SPARKS—WITHINGTON CO.

SPARKS VISIONOLA
RADIO-SOUND MOVIE SET
(Belonged to Clark Gable
and Carol Lombard)
1933

MODEL 2236
TUBES   1936

SPARTON TV-RADIO- PHONO
1949

STEWART WARNER CORP.

SHORT-WAVE CONVERTER ◊
1930

◊ MODEL R-109-A
6 TUBES   1932

ALL-WAVE ◊
5 TUBES. 1934 EST.

RTR, JUNE 1939

DIONNE QUINTUPLETS RADIOS

MODEL 07-5B3Q
7 TUBES   1939

MODEL 07-513Q
7 TUBES   1939

STEWART WARNER CORP.

PORTO BARADIO 9008-B
5 TUBES   1946

AM-FM-CONSOLE
8 TUBES + RECT.
1947

THE AIR PAL
4 TUBES + RECT.   1947

MODEL 9153-A
4 TUBES AC-DC-BATT
1950

MODEL 9150-D
8 TUBES AC-DC-BATT
1950

MODEL T-1210
26 TUBES 12"
RADIO-TV   1939

DIRECT VIEW TV
22 TUBES 10" ◇
1947

177

CUSTOM DELUXE 16
(Model 9120-C)
Huge 16" screen perfect for your TV-only customers! Rich Mahogany; full-length doors! 23 tubes plus 3 rectifiers.

MASTER PANORAMIC 16
(Model 9121-B)
The utmost in home entertainment . . . 16" TV-FM-AM-3-Speed phono. Gracious Mahogany cabinet . . . record storage space. 28 tubes plus 3 rectifiers.

See your Stewart-Warner Distributor Today!

STEWART-WARNER ELECTRIC *Division of Stewart-Warner Corporation* 1826 Diversey Parkway • Chicago 14, Illinois
Canadian Factory: STEWART-WARNER ALEMITE CORPORATION OF CANADA, LTD., Belleville, Ontario

All new for '51!

SPECIAL 14
(Model 9200-A)
Huge 14" screen priced for every budget! Rich Mahogany with forest green leatherette front panel. 17 tubes plus 2 rectifiers.

ROYAL DELUXE 16
(Model 9120-B)
Every home will be proud to own this stunning 16" TV Console! In hand-rubbed Mahogany . . . or lovely Blonde Korina (Model 9120-F). 23 tubes plus 3 rectifiers.

1951

SPECIAL DELUXE 16
(Model 9120-A)
Big 16" screen . . . rich Mahogany styling! The answer to table TV sales—bigger pictures in a smaller cabinet! 23 tubes plus 3 rectifiers.

SUPER DELUXE 16
(Model 9120-D)
Giant 16" screen. Lustrous hand-rubbed Mahogany; smart half-length doors. Also (available in Blonde Korina 9120-E). 23 tubes plus 3 rectifiers.

178

179

No. 225-H

No. 228-H

No. 230-H

No. 240-H

TABLE MODELS IN THE HORIZONTAL STYLE POPULARIZED BY STROMBERG-CARLSON

No. 228-L

No. 230-L

No. 229-P

No. 231-P

No. 240-L

No. 240-M

No. 240-S

No. 240-W

CONSOLES AND FURNITURE MODELS YEARS AHEAD IN BRILLIANCE OF DESIGN

No. 240-R

No. 255-L CONSOLE (at right). Five Range. Flash Tuning. Tri-Focal Tuning Indicator. High Fidelity. Acoustical Labyrinth. Selectorlite Dial. Carpinchoe Speaker. Walnut finish.

No. 250-L

No. 260-L

END TABLE AND COFFEE TABLE MODELS

No. 231-R

No. 231-F

THERE IS NOTHING FINER THAN A
Stromberg-Carlson

180

STROMBERG-CARLSON
TELEPHONE MFG. CO.

MODEL 420R ◊
7 TUBES 1939

◊ MODEL 535-M
AM-FM-SW
8 TUBES 1941

MODEL 535-PG
AM-FM-SW-PHONO ◊
8 TUBES 1941

◊ TS-16-L1 YARMOUTH
TV-FM-AM 12"
1949

TS-125LM WEYMOUTH ◊
TV-FM-AM $565.00
1949

Westinghouse
Complete
RADIO LINE

Standard Wave Compact Model WR-20

Dual Wave Universal Compact Model WR 21

DeLuxe All-Wave Console Model WR-30

Standard and Short-Wave Console Model WR-29

All Wave Table Model WR-23

Standard and Short Wave Table Model WR-28

All-Wave Console Model WR-24

WESTINGHOUSE ELECTRIC CORP.

Westinghouse was a very early radio manufacturer, but sold home sets through RCA until 1930. Westinghouse entered the market in 1930, and introduced its TV set line in the late 1940's.

CANADIAN WESTINGHOUSE
CO. LTD.   754A
6 TUBES,   5 BANDS
1935 EST. ▷

◁ MODEL WR-209
5 TUBES   1936

MODEL WR-258 ▷
5 TUBES   1938

◁ MODEL WR-368
9 TUBES   1938

MODEL H-216M ▷
33 TUBES   1950

Westinghouse
"firsts" have made radio and television history

WESTINGHOUSE Broadcast The World's *FIRST* Radio Program

In 1921, Westinghouse Radio Station KDKA, Pittsburgh, beamed the first radio broadcast in history to a handful of eager listeners. Thus, began the radio industry.

WESTINGHOUSE Built The World's *FIRST* Electronic Television

More than 20 years ago Westinghouse built the first electronic TV set and TV transmitter. And Westinghouse was the first manufacturer licensed to make color television.

▲ **WESTINGHOUSE 226**
Twelve-inch TV set in a smart, compact console. Powerful circuit for long distance reception. *Available at reduced cost with 10" TV tube.*

▲ **WESTINGHOUSE 216**
Giant 16-inch television in a cabinet of classic beauty. Fingertip pressure opens or closes delicately counterbalanced picture unit.

30 YEARS IN RADIO AND TELEVISION MAKE THESE *ALL NEW* SETS POSSIBLE

WESTINGHOUSE ▶
makes a complete line of table-top radios, powered and designed for every taste, and starting at . . .
$19⁹⁵
for model 210 shown

◀ **WESTINGHOUSE**
produces 3 powerful portables for those who want the best in radio entertainment *anywhere*. They start at a low of . . .
$29⁹⁵
for model 185 shown

YOU CAN BE SURE...
IF IT'S Westinghouse

INTERESTING SETS

◊ HERBERT H. HORN
"TIFFANY-TONE"
5 TUBES 1936

LE WOL CORP.
"BEST" 4L ◊
4 TUBES 1934

◊ MIDWEST
"IMPERIAL"
18 TUBES 1935

NATIONAL CO.
MODEL TV-7
$189.50 1948 ◊
(TV-7W, WOOD, $199.50)

◊ POINT OF PURCHASE
DISPLAYS INC.
MODEL 5A/410A
5 TUBES

ZENITH RADIO CORPORATION'S MOBILE RADIO STATION, WJAZ, IN 1925.

ZENITH RADIO CORP.

Cdr. E. F. McDonald, Jr. in 1938

Zenith began as Chicago Radio Labs in 1918, making radio amateur equipment. The name "Zenith" came from 9ZN, the station call of Ralph Matthews and Karl Hassel, co-founders. In 1921 Cdr. Eugene F. McDonald, Jr. joined the group. He guided its growth into one of the three major radio manufacturers of the 1930-1950 era, along with Hugh Robertson as treasurer. The Zenith name first appeared in 1923. Zenith pioneered in short-wave equipment, using Admiral Donald B. Mc-Millan's polar expeditions as the vehicle. This led to a highly successful line of short-wave sets, and helped short-wave communications the world over. Other "firsts" were Zenith's portable radio in 1924, first production A-C radio in 1926, and pushbutton tuning in 1927. The famous "Big Black Dial" first appeared in 1934. Zenith's W9XZV pioneered all-electronic TV broadcasts in 1939, and W9XEN (later WEFM) was one of the first FM stations in 1940. Zenith introduced its TV sets in 1948, based on prototype sets built as early as 1939. Zenith's production philosophy has always been high quality at a price, making their sets good collectors' items.

LOOK FOR THE RADIO
WITH
THE BIG BLACK DIAL

ZENITH
TRADE MARK REG
→ LONG-DISTANCE ← RADIO

ZENITH RADIO CORP.

◊ MODEL 64
(MODEL 60 CHASSIS)
9 TUBES $370.00
1930

MODEL 75
RADIO-PHONOGRAPH ◊
9 TUBES $375.00
1930

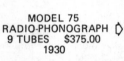

MODEL 245
◊ 9 TUBES   1931

MODEL 441 ◊
12 TUBES
1933

NOW ★ ★ THE

ZENITH

TRADE MARK REG

OF AUTO RADIO

MODEL 460

$59⁹⁵

Complete, including installation equipment, but not installation (aerial equipment when required is extra).

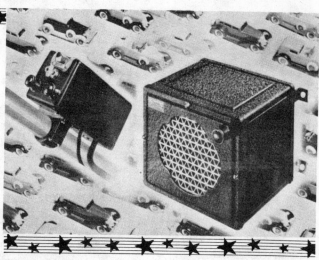

★ Years of research, testing, improving . . . years of forgoing temporary profits which might have been made in the field . . . finally, engineers have produced the Auto Radio that can proudly carry the name, *Zenith*.

Simplicity of installation and brilliant performance have been achieved in the Zenith Auto Set.

External generators, eliminators, and batteries (excepting the one already in the car) have been eliminated. The ease of installation is indicated by the fact that there are but two units to install.

An exclusive Zenith engineering triumph—there is direct and positive drive on the tuning dial. The condensor, located in the control box, eliminates less efficient remote controls. Unique design eliminates vibration detuning after the dial is set. A seven tube superheterodyne with automatic volume control. A lock switch prevents the use of the receiver by unauthorized persons.

Fully tested under the most severe conditions, the Zenith set is now offered dealers with the assurance that it will produce both sales and satisfaction. Write for complete information.

★ ZENITH RADIO CORPORATION, CHICAGO ★

ZENITH RADIO CORP.

◊ MODEL 230
8 TUBES   1933

MODEL 808
SERIES K
6 TUBES   1934   ◊

 ◊ MODEL 665 $49.95
6 TUBES   1935
(5 TUBES, MODEL 664, $39.95)

MODEL 668
6 TUBES $54.95 ◊
1935

◊ MODEL 1117
6 TUBES
1935

ZENITH

The only Radio adjustable for any size room

ZENITH
10-S-160
10 tubes. Tunes American and foreign stations, police, amateur, aviation, ships at sea. Auditorium 12-inch Electro-Dynamic Speaker. 42 inches high. **Price $139.95.**

ZENITH
8-S-154
8 tubes. Tunes American and foreign stations, police, amateur, aviation, ships at sea. Auditorium 12-inch Electro-Dynamic Speaker. 41 inches high. **Price $89.95.**

ZENITH ZEPHYR
6-S-147
6 tubes. Tunes American and foreign stations, police, amateur, aviation, ships at sea. 10-inch Electro-Dynamic Speaker. 23 inches high. **Price $84.95.**

ZENITH COMPACT
6-D-117 (AC-DC)
6 tubes (including ballast tube). Tunes broadcast stations, police, amateur, aviation. 5-inch Electro-Dynamic Speaker, Tone Control. 8¼ inches high. **Price $34.95.**

ZENITH
6-S-128
6 tubes. Tunes American and foreign stations, police, amateur, aviation, ships at sea. 8-inch Electro-Dynamic Speaker. 22 inches high. **Price $59.95.**

ZENITH FARM RADIO
6-B-129
6-tube Superheterodyne. Tunes American and foreign stations, police, amateur, aviation, ships at sea, 8-inch Zenith Dynamic Speaker. Operates on single 6-volt storage battery. 22 inches high. **Price $69.95.**

-a year ahead!

191

ZENITH RADIO CORP.

◊ MODEL 6V 27
6 TUBES + VIBRATOR
6V FARM RADIO
1936

MODEL 7S28 ◊
7 TUBES
1936

◊ MODEL 5529
5 TUBES
1936

MODEL 6S222 ◊
LONG DISTANCE
6 TUBES   1937

ZENITH RADIO CORP.

MODEL 7D127
6 TUBES + BALLAST ◊
$49.95   1937

◊ 9S244 CHAIRSIDE
9 TUBES $109.95
1938

MODEL 1207
10 TUBES   1938 ◊

◊ 8S226 CHAIRSIDE
8 TUBES   1939

193

ZENITH RADIO CORP.

FIRST ZENITH TV
1939

MODEL 5808
8 TUBES   1940

MODEL 5G401
UNIVERSAL PORTABLE
AC-DC-BATT
5 TUBES, $39.95
1940

4K600 POCKETRADIO
4 TUBES BATT'Y
$19.95   1941

7G605 TRANS-OCEANIC
(FIRST OF A QUALITY ALL-WAVE
SERIES. McMILLAN USED PROTOTYPE
IN ARTIC EXPLORATION)
7 TUBES   AC-DC-BATT
1941

ZENITH RADIO CORP.

12S453 CHAIRSIDE
12 TUBES $109.95
"ROBOT DIAL"
"OUTER CIRCLE RF CIRCUIT" ◊
"WAVEMAGNET ANTENNA"
"RADIORGAN"
1945

4K016
◊ 4 TUBES   BATT'Y
1946

5C01 CONSULTONE ◊
5 TUBES   1946

◊ 6D029 LONG DISTANCE
6 TUBES   1946

8G005YT
TRANS-OCEANIC
8 TUBES   AC-DC-BATT ◊
$124.40   1946

ZENITH RADIO CORP.

G2420 MAYFLOWER
ZENITH'S FIRST PRODUCTION TV
11" PORTHOLE $389.95
"GIANT CIRCLE" SCREEN
"BULL'S-EYE" TUNING
1948

MODEL 6G601Y
6 TUBES
$59.60   1948
(OTHER 6G601's in 1941)

MODEL 6G801Y
5 TUBES + RECT.
AC-DC-BATT
1949

5G40 TRANS-OCEANIC
5 TUBES AC-DC-BATT
6 BANDS   1950

MODEL 5G41
AC-DC-PHONO
5 TUBES   1950

RADIO AND TELEVISION RETAILING, MARCH 1950

ZENITH'S NEW 1950 "PRESIDENTIAL" LINE OF *Television*

The Washington. Model G3275R. Superb radio-phono-graph-television, with 165 sq. inches of picture area. In genuine Mahogany veneers. **$625.00***

The Lincoln. Model G2438R. Zenith's new "Super-Range" chassis with Glare-Ban "Black" Picture Tube in handsome new cabinet of genuine Mahogany or Walnut veneers. 165 sq. inches of picture area. **$359.95***

The Madison. Model G3173R. Handsome new combination television-radio-phonograph with "Big B" Giant Circle Screen. Cabinet of genuine Mahogany or Walnut. **$449.95***

The Jackson. Model G2437R. Beautiful new console in genuine Mahogany veneers. "Giant C" Giant Circle Screen plus all Zenith's great chassis features. **$429.95***

The Fillmore. Model G2437E. Stunning new style in lustrous blonde-finished cabinet. "Giant C" Giant Circle Screen—165 sq. inches of picture area. **$439.95***

The Monroe. Model G2439R. New Zenith Console with Glare-Ban "Black" Picture Tube—165 sq. inches of picture area. Gorgeous cabinet of genuine Mahogany veneers. **$399.95***

The Adams. Model G2350R. Choice of genuine Walnut or Mahogany veneers in new Zenith Console. "Big B" Giant Circle Screen. With Blaxide "Black" Picture Tube. **$269.95***

The Garfield. Model G2327. Popular Table Model in smart, long-wearing Walnut Brown Pyroxylin. "Big B" Giant Circle Screen plus new "Super-Range" chassis. **$219.95***

The Harrison. Model G2356R. New console brings the utmost in picture quality in a "Big B" Giant Circle Screen. 18th Century cabinet of genuine Mahogany veneers. **$309.95***

The Tyler. Model G2355E. Greater distance, greater clarity in this striking console with 105 sq. inches of picture area. In handsome blonde finish. **$289.95***

*Plus Federal Excise Tax. Prices subject to change without notice. West Coast and Far South prices slightly higher.

Look to Zenith FIRST with the Finest in Television!

RADIO & TE

197

OFF TO THE HAMFEST —

—AND BACK HOME AGAIN

CHAPTER IV
AMATEUR RADIO

If you're a Ham, this chapter will help recapture the old days, when a good code "fist" was highly respected and your own personal craftsmanship went into your rig. If you're not a Ham, this chapter will help you appreciate the guy in your neighborhood with the tall tower and the weird array of wires spun around the premises.

All too often, the neighborhood Ham is known only for suspected interference with your favorite television program. Actually, Ham radio has contributed greatly to the welfare of all of us. If there's a natural catastrophe, your neighborhood Ham is likely to be your only contact with the outside world. If there's an international emergency, he (or she) is likely to be pressed into uniform or made part of the War Emergency Radio Service. If you can't get an important message to someone far away by normal means, chances are that a Ham in your town can get it through for you. It's hard to visualize a hobby that is this much fun and yet has so much potential for good public service.

Let's turn the clock back a few years. You've just received that long-awaited Ham license in the mail. Your first station "rig" has been ready for weeks. Today is the day! Proudly and more than a little nervously you tune up your transmitter: "Dah dit dit-dit-dit dah" you tap out and fiddle with the knobs, watching your plate current meter and that little light bulb in the grid circuit. Now you are ready! Here we go – CQ CQ CQ de W6TPE (or whatever that brand-new call might be). Sooner or later a reply comes chirping back across the miles, and you experience that supreme one-time thrill that only a Ham knows. This is your first of many contacts, and life will never be quite the same.

Maybe, after this first QSO, you sit back and remember that long, hard struggle to get your "ticket". There were all those hours straining to build your code speed up for the big test, with maybe a little to spare. Then there were all those frequencies to memorize. There were other small facts too, like the penalties

Date of issuance: UNITED STATES OF AMERICA NOT
2-1-41 FEDERAL COMMUNICATIONS COMMISSION TRANSFERABLE
WASHINGTON

AMATEUR RADIO OPERATOR LICENSE

This license when signed by an issuing officer of the Commission, indicating privileges granted and countersigned by the Licensee, is valid for 3 years from the date of issuance, subject to the provisions of all treaties, laws, orders, and regulations that apply to amateur radio operators.

FEDERAL COMMUNICATIONS COMMISSION,
Licensee and P. O. address: T. J. Slowie, *Secretary.*

Morgan Edson McMahon
3374 Madera Ave.
Oakland, Calif.

Privileges	Issuing Officer	Date
Class C		
Class B		
Class A		

FCC 660 UNITED STATES OF AMERICA NOT
FEDERAL COMMUNICATIONS COMMISSION TRANSFERABLE
WASHINGTON N

AMATEUR RADIO STATION LICENSE

This license is valid until 3 o'clock a. m., eastern standard time, 3 years from date of issuance, subject to the provisions of all treaties, laws, orders, and regulations that apply to amateur radio stations.

Licensee and fixed station location: Call letters:

Morgan Edson McMahon W 6 T P E
3374 Madera Ave. Date of
Oakland, Calif. issuance:

2-1-41

This license vests no right to operate the station nor to the use of authorized frequencies beyond the term hereof, nor in any other manner than authorized herein. This license is subject to the right of use or control by the Government of the United States under section 606 of the Communications Act of 1934.

FEDERAL COMMUNICATIONS COMMISSION,
T. J. Slowie, *Secretary.*

THE TICKET TO ADVENTURE

QST, MAY 1944

YOU MAY RECOGNIZE SOME OF THESE

200

for infractions of the laws; was that $10,000 and two years in jail or $2000 and ten years in jail? Better have it down cold for the exam! And all that theory — Let's see; that neutralizing condenser went from where to where?

Anyhow, there was the BIG DAY when you made your trek to the FCC office or the Post Office to face the Radio Inspector. First there was the code test, and chances were pretty good that you'd have to come back again to take another crack at it. Then there was the written test, and the long, long wait at your mailbox. Some people have been known to tune their transmitters on the air before the ticket arrived or even to "bootleg" on 5 meters, sort of like lovers before the wedding.

The rewards of Ham radio are great and varied. There's the adventure of sending out a CQ and seeing who, from where, answers. It might be from the other side of the Globe, or might be an old rag-chewing friend whom you haven't heard from in years. Or, you answer someone else's CQ and hope that he'll come back. There are also the "scheds" when you talk with air-wave friends on a regular schedule. There are the nets, where you can do a great public service by forwarding personal messages for the general public. It's also very rewarding to set up a direct contact between your neighbors and their relatives far away, and to watch their eyes light up at the sound of a familiar voice. We never wish for catastrophe, but it's nice to know that our Ham shack can become the center of communications if other systems are wiped out.

Then there's the fun of the Ham-fest or field day, where you can have nose-to-nose QSO's with your air friends, and maybe even win the hidden-transmitter contest. You can find all kinds of goodies at the Ham-fest swap meet, and may sell that old dog of a transmitter in the bargain.

Contests were (and still are) a big part of Ham life. It is great fun to get the most foreign QSO's in a time period, or to squeak the greatest distance out of that 2 meter rig. It was great to get that worked-all-states certificate before your friendly competitors made the grade, too.

Your Ham shack and your mobile rig are prized possessions. You sink every available (?) cent into hardware, and then become an amateur scientist to squeeze the most out of it. The

201

antenna system becomes an exercise in gymnastics as you try to get that new beam into the sky. You may even have to become an expert in public relations as neighbors scream at this latest intrusion into local airspace.

Be our guest. Take time to wander through this chapter, re-capturing the flavor of those old Ham radio days. You might also think of Bob Morris (W2LV) who did much of the background work, and Don Elliott, who wrote the following sections.

IN THE BEGINNING (1901-1928)

"Amateur Radio" was born immediately following Marconi's successful spanning of the Atlantic in 1901. Everyone——commercial and amateur alike——got on the air. The limited knowledge available dictated use of long wavelengths and maximum antenna current. A few well-heeled amateurs boasted stations that surpassed many commercial installations, but the majority were content with exchanging greetings with others in nearby cities using the most modest of purchased or home built apparatus.

The simplest equipment was available for transmitting; spark coil, spark gap, battery supply, telegraph key, antenna, and a good ground connection. Later, a condenser and tapped antenna coil arranged in a "closed oscillating circuit" could be added to increase the signal strength and permit a limited tuning ability. For still greater power and range the spark coil could be replaced by a large power transformer energized from the 110-volt power er mains in conjunction with a suitable motor-driven interrupter. Also, the simple spark gap satisfactory for the lower power sets was usually replaced by a rotary spark gap better suited to the higher voltages available, or an arc or quenched gap could give a clean, beautiful transmitted signal.

The receiver accompanying the spark transmitter was equally unsophisticated. Usually it began as a three-slide tuning coil, crystal or electrolytic detector, head-phones with by-pass capacitor, and a suitable antenna switch to permit one antenna to suffice for either transmitting or receiving. More fortunate amateurs might have one of DeForest's audion tubes as the detector or amplifier.

"Wireless clubs" sprang up in most major cities. The Radio

QST, AUGUST 1932

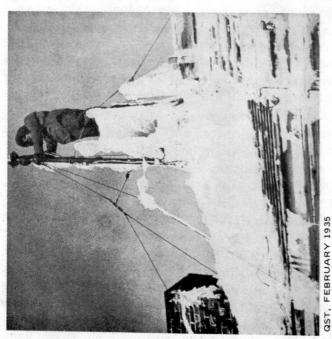

QST, FEBRUARY 1935

203

Club of America was organized in 1909 and is still going strong. Hugo Gernsback, famed publisher of radio periodicals, sponsored the Radio League of America, to name another. With the advent of the American Radio Relay League (ARRL) founded by Hiram Percy Maxim in 1914, the means existed for amateurs to look to themselves for technical advancement, improved operating techique and legislative impact. The ARRL organized relay trunk lines from coast to coast. Through its journal, QST, Maxim and the ARRL became the principal spokesman for amateur affairs.

America's entry in World War I closed down amateur radio until 1919 but many amateurs operated military stations and impressed government officials with the value of this new national resource—an impression that was instrumental in safeguarding the hobby in the countless national and international communication conferences that were to follow.

The decade following WW I began with amateurs assigned 200-250 meters. By 1925, the familiar amateur bands (160–80–40–20–10– and 5 meters) had been assigned.

COMING OF AGE (1929-1934)

Retaining but 53 percent of the pre-1929 frequency spectrum, amateur radio came of age by the mid-thirties. This is exemplified by the fact that by 1935 the "relative density" of stations per kilocycle was over 8 times the 1929 figure, yet overall operating conditions and enjoyment of the hobby were vastly improved.

How this seeming paradox came about is an interesting tale.

To begin, a better understanding of transmitters was a prerequisite. In particular, the factors affecting frequency stability for self-controlled oscillators had to be explored and explained in some detail. Fortunately, Ross Hull of the QST staff did yeoman service in this regard. His coined term, "High-C", to achieve stable tank circuit operation, became a common, well-understood criterion for post-29 "home-brew" equipment.

The typical CW rig, at the start, was a single tube self-controlled oscillator employing either type '10 or '03A tubes with 25 to 100 watts input. Basic Hartley, Colpitts, Ultraaudion and Tuned-Plate-Tuned-Grid circuits or variations thereof were about equally popular. One such variation of the last named circuit

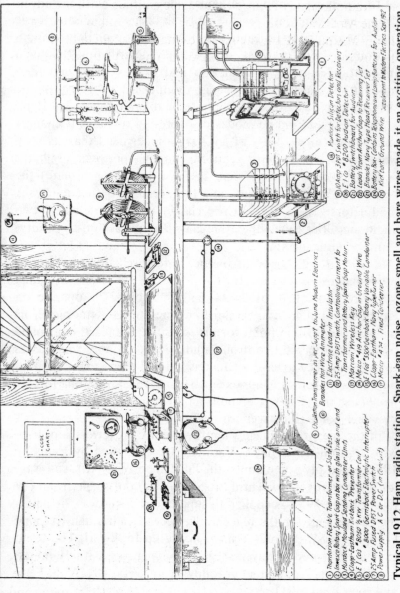

① Thordarson Fleurle Transformer or Slate Base
② Imexco Rotary Spark Gap in box with glass side and end
③ Murdock-Mosier Sending Condenser Units
④ Clapp-Eastham Kickback Preventer
⑤ E I Co. "8050 ½ KW Transformer Coil
⑥ E I Co. "8000 Germback Electrolytic Interrupter
⑦ 25 Amp Fused DPST Power Switch
⑧ Power-Supply A C or D C (in Com'on't)

⑨ Oscillation Transformer as per Scopt Volume Modern Electrics
⑩ Brandes Hot Wire Ammeter
⑪ Electrode Lead-in Insulator
⑫ 25 Amp DPST Switch, Controlling Current to Transformer and Rotary Spark Gap Motor.
⑬ Marconi Wireless Key
⑭ Mesco "419 Anchor Gap or Ground Wire
⑮ E I Co. "1300 Germback Rotary Variable Condenser
⑯ Clapp-Eastham Navy Type Tuner
⑰ Mesco "434 Fixed Condenser

⑱ 10 Amp, 3P3T Switch for Detectors and Receivers
⑲ E I Co. "8200 Audion Detector
⑳ Battery Switchboard for Audion
㉑ Leads from Anchor Gap to Receiving Set
㉒ Brandes Navy Type Head Receiver Set
㉓ Battery Box-Contains Telephone and Batteries for Audion
㉔ Klee Eastham Telephone and Batteries for Audion
㉕ Kick back Ground Wire   Supplement to Modern Electrics Sept 1912

Typical 1912 Ham radio station. Spark-gap noise, ozone smell and bare wires made it an exciting operation.

was called the "TNT" (tuned, not tuned) because it eliminated the variable tuning capacitor otherwise required in the grid circuit. The most common antennas were the long wire, the off-center-fed "Windom," or the end-fed "Zepp". The same basic one-tube oscillator transmitter employing loop or Heising modulation sufficed for what was passingly described as "phone". Incidental frequency modulation and usually over- or under-modulation caused most "brass pounders" to consider the "phone men" as a separate, only to be tolerated, breed of Ham.

Both CW and phone modes of operation underwent changes and improvement. First of all, having recognized that stability went hand-in-hand with reduced coupling between oscillator and antenna, amplifiers were inserted to buffer (isolate) the oscillator. In 'phone operation the former inefficient class-A modulators gave way to RCA's class-B modulators, where two audio amplifier tubes operating class B duplicate up to twenty-four operating class A.

Again, in 1933, advent of the tri-tet oscillator marked another major step forward; for the first time, practically speaking, a crystal-controlled oscillator had the ability to operate on either the fundamental crystal frequency or its harmonics. This marked the turning point for the transition from self-controlled oscillators to crystal control. In addition, the same year, it was ruled mandatory to have adequately filtered plate power supplies on all stages for all bands except 10 and 5 meters. Gone forever would be the distinctive audio modulation of their CW signals by which some Hams were so readily recognized.

In the meantime, steady improvement of receivers kept pace with transmitter changes. Various sets were used by Hams by 1930, especially home builts, the Pilot Super Wasp Kit, and Nat-ional Company's new Thrill Box. The advent of single signal CW reception in 1932 as applied to superheterodynes was the beginning of the end for the regenerative receiver, although National Company's SW-3 would remain in use up to WW II. The trend to manufactured receivers began, commencing with Hammarlund's Comet Pro, and soon followed by National's AGS, FB-7 and long lived HRO series.

Natural disasters took their usual toll, but in every instance amateur radio assisted in relief operations. Probably a record

EARLY HAM TRANSMITTERS

◁ TUNED-PLATE TUNED-GRID
"HI-C" TANK CIRCUIT
552 TUBE   75W
1930

2-TUBE TNT
45's OR 210's ◁
1930

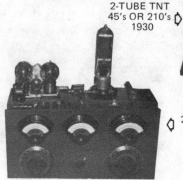

◁ 2 205D's AND 211D
W2BGN   1930

M. O. P. A.
160 METERS ◁
210 -- 210
W6BGN 1930

◁ UNITY-COUPLED PUSH-PULL
CRYSTAL OSCILLATOR
80M 210's --45's
W2AFE 1934 ARRL HNDBK.

6L6-6L6-PP 809's ◁
W1PEG   1936

◁ FIVE METER RECEIVER
230 SUPER-REGEN. DETECTOR
231 AUDIO AMPLIFIER
W1JJE   1937

207

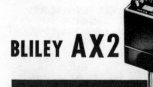

BLILEY AX2 — *First for amateur frequencies*

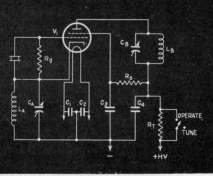
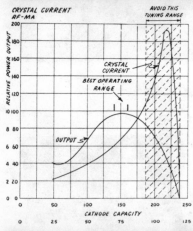

was established by W6BYF of Long Beach, California, who was on the air within 10 minutes following the major California earthquake in 1933.

MATURITY (1935-1941)

The balance of years remaining until WW II closed all Ham shacks "for the duration" saw a steady increase in the number of amateurs. In spite of the Depression, there was a flow of commercial gear tailored to the needs and wants of the hobby. For the same money, an amateur station could be had that far surpassed in performance an equivalent 1929 investment. A definite trend to commercial "communications" receivers was noted while, parodoxically, "home-brew" transmitters remained in favor with the majority. Most activity was still on the 160, 80, 40 and 20 meter bands. The super-regenerative receiver, together with a voice-modulated oscillator, had been demonstrated as an ideal experimental 10, 5 and 2½ meter station. It wasn't until the ARRL conducted two UHF relays in 1938, however, that real progress began.

Instead, major attention remained on the lower frequencies and no wonder! Metal tubes and 6-volt tubes were available in almost unlimited variety. One "workhorse", the 6L6 beam-power tube originally intended for audio work, together with the 807 transmitting tube, was the basis for many low-power crystal-oscillator transmitter for the pre-war years. The "QSL-40" was about the simplest one-tube crystal-controlled CW transmitter ever devised.

Also, several major improvements in receiver design appeared during this period. Principal among them was the introduction of Lamb's IF noise silencer in 1936, a circuit refinement which is still found today in some receivers. Also, the first practical iron core IF transformers appeared in 1935. The ARRL handbooks of the period still extolled "home-brew", describing all-band circuits still employing plug-in coils in contrast to band-switching arrangements offered by the trade.

Initial articles on television began appearing in late 1937. Commercially feasible TV was still "around the corner" although some Hams did get involved in experimental equipment, especially after the Cario conference allocated 112-, 224- and 300 Mc

ROTARY BEAM ANTENNAS

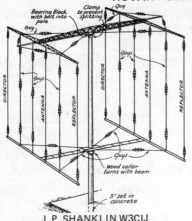

J. P. SHANKLIN W3CIJ
14 MC VERTICALLY POLARIZED
JULY 1934

20 meter and shorter bands became really practical when rotary beams were built. Basic systems were devised in the mid-30's, and beam technology was quite sophisticated by 1950.

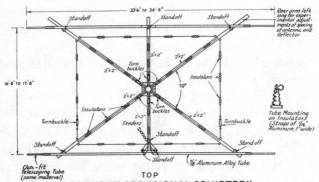

TOP
M-P-MIMS W5 BDB "SIGNAL SQUIRTER"
14 MC HORIZONTALLY POLARIZED BEAM
DECEMBER 1935

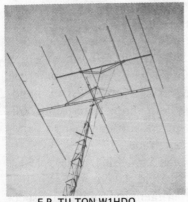

E.P. TILTON W1HDQ
6 & 10 METER ARRAY
JULY 1947

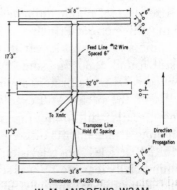

W. M. ANDREWS, W3AM
14 MC BINOMIAL-CURRENT ARRAY
JULY 1950

bands for amateur use. The first American two-way amateur television QSO took place in September, 1940 at the New York World's Fair.

At high frequencies, the old wire antenna standby dating from the late '20's was being replaced by beam arrays. A 14 Mc rotatable array appeared in 1934 and Mim's 14 Mc "Signal Squirter" followed the next year. Multiband antennas comprising dipoles tied together and fed by a 75 ohm line came along in 1937, while 3-element rotary beam arrays employing slip rings or inductive coupling (in lieu of the then non-existent coax line) were the last word.

A battle for allocating part of the 40-meter band for 'phone raged within the ranks. As of 1938, 68 percent of all Hams polled said "NO". It wouldn't be until 1952 that 'phone would be so permitted.

THE WAR YEARS(1942-1945)

The major division of amateur activity during WW II comprised either military service or participation in the War Emergency Radio Service (WERS) administered by the Civil Defense Corps. Initially, the ARRL-sponsored Emergency Corps formed in 1935 was permitted to continue in operation. Although exercising self-discipline to avoid any communications comparable to peacetime QSO's, fear by authorities that it would get out of hand caused its early demise in January 1942.

Station equipment was not only shut down, but, if it comprised commercial gear, it was purchased on the spot by traveling teams of military officers seeking to augment the production from manufacturers.

THE POST WAR PERIOD (1946-1950)

Immediately on the heels of peace came the formal petitions to lift the ban on amateur operations. Although the Loran service caused the temporary loss of the 160 meter band, and television's Channel 2 inherited the old 5-meter band, the amateur service fared very well. The 80, 40-, and 20 meter bands were returned intact. 10 meters was reduced 300 Kc. A new 6 meter band replaced the loss of 5 meters. The 2½ meter band was shifted to 2 meters and several micro-wave bands were allocated for

Type No.	Approx. grid drive (watts)	Max. d-c plate input (watts)	Max. d-c plate volts	Max. freq. at Max. ratings (Mc)	Amateur net price
2E26	0.2	40	600	125	$3.50
807	0.2	75	750	60	2.30
813	4	500	2250	30	14.50
815	0.2	75	500	125	6.25
828	2.2	270	1500	30	12.50
829-B	0.8	150	750	200	14.75
832-A	0.2	36	750	200	10.60

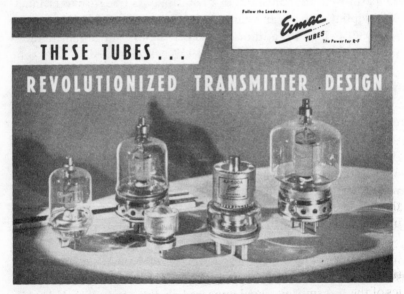

Follow the Leaders to

Eimac
TUBES
The Power for R-F

THESE TUBES . . .
REVOLUTIONIZED TRANSMITTER DESIGN

TUBES WERE THE KEY TO TRANSMITTER ADVANCEMENT

212

amateur use.

"Home brew" equipment and early surplus gear was put on the air immediately while waiting for the "new" post-war equipment promised during the war years by the majority of manufacturers. In the main, the first such gear was a rehash of 1941 technology dressed in 1946 cabinetry. Metal tubes predominated; IF design still centered around 455 Kc; and single crystal selectivity was a standard feature on most of the better receivers.

Surplus equipment increased in quantity and ingenious modification schemes for amateur utilization appeared. For one example, propeller pitch-control motors were adapted for rotating 20 and 10-meter antenna beams. To permit control from the Ham shack, a pair of selsyns were installed as direction indicators. For another; the BC 312 receiver was combined with the "Q5-er" to achieve selectivity far greater than any available in commercial equipment.

Narrow-band FM on 75 and 20 meters was approved but never became popular. Too few amateurs acquired the necessary adapters for their AM receivers.

Perhaps the two major post-war areas of technical interest were those of single side-band and television interference. As to the first, it had long been known that transmitting the carrier was wasteful of transmitted power as was also the transmission of both sidebands. By one means of reckoning, a 100-watt single sideband transmitter would equal the performance of a 400-watt AM transmitter. This factor, together with the narrow transmission band occupied by the SSB system, offered much promise for amateur application. As a consequence, the change over from AM to SSB began in earnest; in 1950, Collins revamped their 75A AM receiver of 1946 and heralded the 75 Al as the "Sideband receiver of the year." This trend, together with rebirth of the SSB transceiver operating simplex to replace the separate transmitter and receiver, resulted in the maximum utilization of the spectrum as enjoyed today.

On the other hand, television interference, or TVI, was a knotty problem that literally caused hundreds of amateur stations to cease operations. The problem was two-fold; harmonics of the transmitted signal appeared on the newly assigned television channels and many inexpensive or poorly designed TV receivers were susceptible to this interference. Much of the literature of the late '40's was devoted to eliminating this problem. The concerted effort of amateurs on the one hand and higher standards for TV receiver design on the other combined to eventually put the problem to rest.

The cubical quad antenna array made its appearance in 1948. A most useful device – the "Micromatch" – permitting the instantaneous measurement of the standing wave ratio on a transmission line, was introduced about the same time.

AMATEUR RADIO EQUIPMENT, 1930-1950

In preceding paragraphs, we saw the role of equipment in the advance of Amateur radio. At the risk of repetition, let's take a look at receivers and transmitters specifically, as an introduction to our "mug-shot" gallery of historical hardware.

Amateur radio in the period starting in 1930 was undergoing rapid changes in equipment and technology. During the middle and late twenties, most amateur radio stations were homemade from commercially available tubes, parts and components. Pictures and descriptions of stations in QST or Radio News were frequently the guide to design and construction of new transmitters and receivers. Most transmitters in 1930 were self-excited oscillators exhibiting varied degrees of frequency stability depending upon the skill of the operator. Receivers, with very few exceptions, were regenerative using filament type tubes with battery supplies.

Before 1930, with the exception of early Grebe, Paragon, Mignon, DeForest or other commercial receivers, most amateur receivers were home-made regenerative sets using d-c filaments type tubes and commercial components. By 1930 most of the Grebes, Paragons, etc. had been retired because of growing interest in shorter wavelengths (20, 40 and 80 meters). Pilot's Super Wasp was the most popular Ham set going into the 1930's. National's famous Thrill Box line was first offered in 1929, and became the Ham's mainstay in the early thirties. National, Hallicrafters, Hammarlund and RME dominated amateur receiver markets in the thirties and forties, along with Breting, Collins, Howard, Patterson, REL and RCA.

Early-1920's transmitter with a priceless collection of early QSL cards. R-F tube lineup is 202-202-203; modulator is 301-202-203. Antique Wireless Association Museum, Holcomb, N.Y.

Bill Biddle K8UZ at the microphone of A. W. A.'s early-1920's Ham shack.

Transmitters were also manufactured for amateur service. There was less acceptance of "store-bought" transmitters than receivers during the earlier days. The Ham's favorite form of self-expression was to create his own rig, and he could save money in the process. However, many rigs were built and sold by Collins, Hallicrafters, Harvey, E. F. Johnson, Leeds, RCA, REL, RME and Temco. As single-sideband became popular, circuit complexity forced most amateurs to buy kits or ready-made transmitters.

The great variety of transmitters and receivers made in the 1930-1950 era appears in the following pages. Original prices shown include tubes but usually exclude extras such as separate speakers. Year shown is that of introduction, best as we can determine from magazines, brochures and sales records.

The advance of amateur radio was made possible by improvements in basic building blocks; mikes, tubes, keys, crystals, r-f elements, filters, antenna systems and all the other components. Space doesn't permit attention to them in this book, but you might keep components in mind as great collectibles.

Have a pleasant trip through the picture gallery. No doubt you'll see some old friends.

QST

For the 'Phone Cause

Five crystal-controlled stations which contributed much to the success of the 'phone relay work. There is no doubting the upward trend in 'phone station equipment indicated by these typical examples

Top — W7ANT, using a modulated Type '52 amplifier — the modulator a W.E. 212-D tube. A suggestion of the antenna pole and station location is given in the upper left illustration.
Right center — A Type '03-A amplifier at W5PP is modulated by a W.E. 212-D.
Lower right — At W3WI the modulator is a W.E. 211-D. A Type '10 tube is the modulated amplifier.
Alongside W3WI — A pair of W.E. 211-E tubes modulate a single 211-E amplifier at W8AKW.
Lower left — Again, at W9ESL, a W.E. 212-D modulates a Type '03-A.

1931 HAM SHACKS

What was that about a High-Power Holiday?

Most of the stations on this page are still hard at work

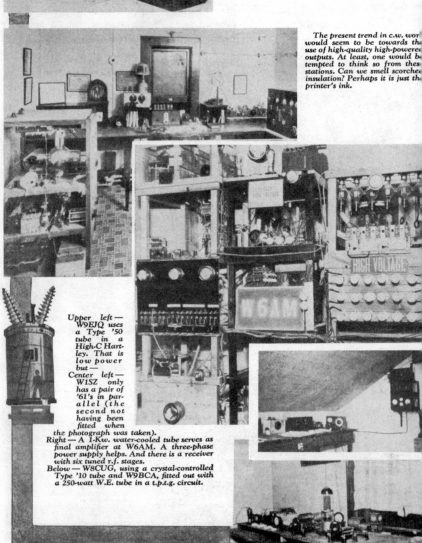

The present trend in c.w. work would seem to be towards the use of high-quality high-powered outputs. At least, one would be tempted to think so from these stations. Can we smell scorched insulation? Perhaps it is just the printer's ink.

Upper left — W9EJQ uses a Type '50 tube in a High-C Hartley. That is low power but —
Center left — W1SZ only has a pair of '61's in parallel (the second not having been fitted when the photograph was taken).
Right — A 1-Kw. water-cooled tube serves as final amplifier at W6AM. A three-phase power supply helps. And there is a receiver with six tuned r.f. stages.
Below — W8CUG, using a crystal-controlled Type '10 tube and W9BCA, fitted out with a 250-watt W.E. tube in a t.p.t.g. circuit.

1931 HAM SHACKS

Prominent in the C.W. Ranks

Some typical stations which competed in the interests of the key

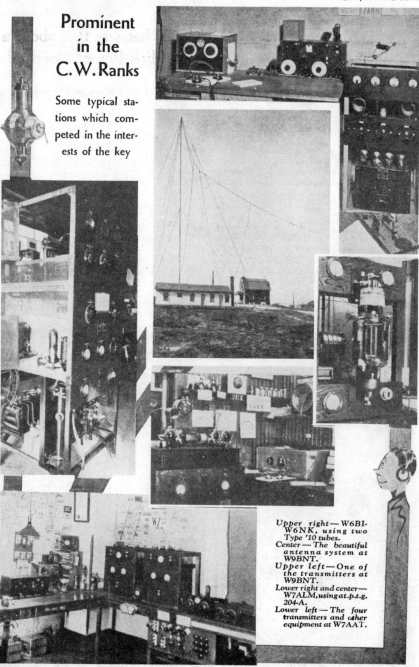

Upper right — W6BI-W6NK, using two Type '10 tubes.
Center — The beautiful antenna system at W9BNT.
Upper left — One of the transmitters at W9BNT.
Lower right and center — W7ALM, using a t.p.t.g. 204-A.
Lower left — The four transmitters and other equipment at W7AAT.

1931 HAM SHACKS

HAM ☆
☆ SHACKS

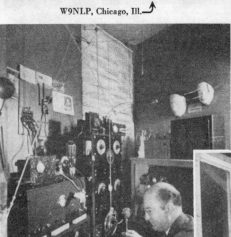

W9NLP, Chicago, Ill.↗

SU1AM, Heliopolis, Egypt↗
← W9SZW, Chicago, Ill.
ZL1MR, Auckland, N. Z.↘

1940 HAM SHACKS

W5GEL

W8OFN

W2JRE

VE5AEC

W6SIG

W6RBQ

W6OZC

XE1A

1946 HAM SHACKS

Presenting the
new Collins 75A-2

**After giving the new 75A-2 a thorough workout, our severest critic, Art Collins WØCXX, said:
"It's a hot receiver — I'll buy it." He is shown here with the 32V-2 and (right) the new 75A-2.**

noticeable improvement. The stability of the BFO is also improved.

The 70E-12 VFO employs a new Collins permeability tuned two-tube circuit, which assures improved stability unaffected by variations in tubes.

Headphone Terminals have been added at the rear of the chassis for operators who wish to avoid having a cord across the operating desk. The headphone jack on the front panel is retained.

The Net Amateur Price of the 75A-2, complete with tubes, $420.00; 10-inch speaker in matching cabinet, $20.00.

Deliveries to Collins distributors will begin October, 1950.

COLLINS AMATEUR RECEIVERS

75A
80-10 METERS ◊
1946

75A-1
◊ 160-10 METERS
$375   1948
PROMOTED IN 1950
AS SSB "RECEIVER
OF THE YEAR."

51J-1
0.5 - 30.5 MC ◊
30 BANDS $875
1949

224

HALLICRAFTERS AMATEUR RECEIVERS

SUPER SKY RIDER
.545-62MC. 11 TUBES ◊
JANUARY '35

◊ SUPER SKY RIDER
7 TUBES
EARLY 1936

ULTRA SKY RIDER
3.9-46M   (LATER 3.76-53M) ◊
10 TUBES
MARCH '36

◊ SKY BUDDY
.544-16.5 MC
5 TUBES
SEPTEMBER '36

NEW 1937
SUPER SKY RIDER
.535-40 MC ◊
11 TUBES
SEPTEMBER '36

◊ SKY CHIEF
.54-17.6 MC
7 TUBES
SEPTEMBER '36

225

HALLICRAFTERS RECEIVERS

◊ SKY RIDER COMMERCIAL
30-3000 M
SEPTEMBER '36

SKY CHALLENGER
9 TUBES
FEBRUARY '37 ◊

1938 SUPER SKY RIDER
5-550 M
◊ 11 TUBES $99.00
JUNE '37

SX-16 SUPER SKY RIDER
5-550 M (-542-62 MC)
11 TUBES $123.00 ◊
APRIL '38

SX-17 SUPER SKY RIDER
◊ 5-550 M   13 TUBES
APRIL ' 38

HALLICRAFTERS AMATEUR RECEIVERS

SKY CHALLENGER II
(S-18, SX-18)
.545-38MC.   9 TUBES
$99.00   FEBRUARY 1938

SKY CHAMPION
.545-44MC.
8 TUBES $49.50
MAY 1938

SKY BUDDY
.545-44MC.
5 TUBES $29.50
MAY 1938

SKYRIDER 23
11 TUBES   MARCH 1939

SX-24 SKYRIDER DEFIANT
.54-43.5 MC.
9 TUBES $69.50
JULY 1939

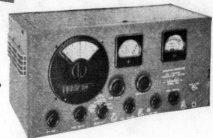

227

HALLICRAFTERS AMATEUR RECEIVERS

SKYRIDER 5—10
27-68 MC   8 TUBES
JULY '39

SUPER DEFIANT (SX-25)
.54-42MC   12 TUBES $99.50
FEBRUARY '40

S-29 SKY TRAVELER
.542-30.5MC 9 TUBES $59.50
AUGUST '40

S-30 RADIO COMPASS
DIRECTION FINDER
200-1500KC $99.50
6 TUBES AUGUST '40

SKYRIDER 32 (SX-32)
.5-30MC   13 TUBES
AUGUST '41

HALLICRAFTERS AMATEUR RECEIVERS

S-27 UHF COMM. RCVR.
28-142MC AM/FM
15 TUBES
FALL 1941 ▷

SX-28 SUPER SKYRIDER
.55-42MC
15 TUBES
FALL 1941

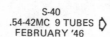

S-40
.54-42MC 9 TUBES ▷
FEBRUARY '46

S-38
.54-32MC
◁ 6 TUBES $39.50
JUNE '46

S-53
.54-54-5MC
8 TUBES $79.50 ▷
FEBRUARY '48

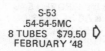

229

HALLICRAFTERS AMATEUR RECEIVERS

SX-42
27-108MC FM
.54-55MC AM
$295.00
SEPTEMBER '48

SX-43
44-55 & 88-108MC FM
.54-55MC AM
SEPTEMBER '48

SX-62
.54-110MC
16 TUBES
BUILT-IN FREQ. CALIBRATOR
APRIL '49

SX-71
.54-35 & 46-56 MC
13 TUBES $179.50
DECEMBER '49

S-40B/S-77
S-40B is IMPROVED S-40
S-77 is AC-DC VERSION
.54-44MC
8 TUBES $79.95
AUG '50 / DEC '50

231

HAMMARLUND AMATEUR RECEIVERS

Hammarlund Comet Pro (above) was first available in early 1932. Early amateur superhet with 8 tubes, 14-200 meters. First available in walnut cabinet, then metal.

FIRST OF THE
FAMOUS "SUPER PRO"
LINE 1.16-20MC
14 TUBES JULY '36 ◊

1937 SUPER-PRO
BAND OPTIONS:
◊ .54-20MC or 1.25-40MC or
15-2000 METERS WITH
2.5-5MC OMITTED.
16 TUBES
MAY '37

HQ-120
.54-31MC
12 TUBES ◊
DECEMBER '38

HAMMARLUND AMATEUR RECEIVERS

NEW SERIES 200
SUPER PRO
1.25-40MC
16 TUBES
JANUARY 1940

HQ-120X1
.54-31MC
12 TUBES
FALL 1941

HQ-129-X
.54-31MC
11 TUBES $129.00
OCTOBER 1945

QST, DECEMBER 1931

For Amateurs Only

This new three-tube Ham receiver bristles with original and ingenious features. Its efficiency and ease of handling will be a revelation to everyone who employs it.

Read R-Rating Direct

The attenuation control is arranged so that angle of rotation is directly proportional to the R-Rating of signal intensity. Control wheel is so mounted that it may be operated by the hand that does the tuning. This is a new and exclusive feature.

NEW! the NATIONAL SW-3 HAM RECEIVER

A three-tube head set receiver with one stage of AF, for full A.C. or storage battery operation with 6 v. heater tubes. A.C. model uses two 235 tubes. **EXTREMELY HIGH SIGNAL TO NOISE RATIO**—a feature of the SW-3. **EXTREME STABILITY AT POINT OF MAXIMUM SENSITIVITY.** Employing hitherto unknown feature of 235 tubes, the point of maximum sensitivity is approached along inverse exponential curve, giving stable operation without critical setting of control.

TRUE SINGLE CONTROL. Easy to tune and log. **ALL COILS WOUND ON R-39**, especially developed for NATIONAL CO. by the Radio Frequency Laboratories, practically eliminating dielectric losses in coil fields. **AMATEUR BAND-SPREAD COILS STANDARD EQUIPMENT.** Free from fringe-howl. Compact: 9¾" x 9¾" x 7", specially suitable also for portable aircraft and boat use. **THE PRICE IS RIGHT.**

Write for Bulletin SW-3T

NATIONAL

235

NATIONAL CO. AMATEUR RECEIVERS

SW-4 THRILL BOX
15-300M   4 TUBES ◊
JULY 1929

A-C SW-5 THRILL BOX
◊ 2.61-21.2MC   5 TUBES
OCTOBER 1930

SW-3 HAM RECEIVER
10-300M, LATER 10-3000M
3 TUBES
OCTOBER, 1931 ◊

A-C SW-5 THRILL BOX
9-2000M   5 TUBES
◊ VARIABLE - MU TUBES
NOVEMBER 1931

NC-5 S-W CONVERTER
15-185M   5 TUBES
NOVEMBER 1931 ◊

HFC
◊ 5-METER CONVERTER
3 TUBES   AUGUST 1932

236

NATIONAL AMATEUR RECEIVERS

◊ **AGS SUPERHET**
2.4-15 MC 11 TUBES
OCTOBER 1932
(AGS-X with crystal filter,
AGU with single-unit plug-in
coils, and AGL long-wave
model all introduced July 1933)

FB-7 SUPERHET
7 TUBES
MARCH 1933 ◊

FBX
SINGLE-SIGNAL SUPERHET
◊ **WITH CRYSTAL FILTER**
1.5-19.5MC 7 TUBES
APRIL 1933

HRO
1.7-30MC 9 TUBES+PWR. SUPP.
OCTOBER 1934
(HRO Junior, without
S-meter and crystal filter ◊
introduced February 1936.
HRO-5 with L-F Coils intro-
duced 1946.)

ONE-TEN
◊ **SUPER-REGENERATIVE**
1-10 METERS 4 TUBES
$85.00 POWER UNIT $29.50
MAY 1936

NATIONAL CO. AMATEUR RECEIVERS

NC-100 (SERIES)
.54-30MC   12 TUBES
$200.00   SEPTEMBER 1936
(Also NC-100X with
Crystal Filter) ▷

NC-101X
10-160 METER BANDSPREAD
VERSION OF NC-100X.
▷   12 TUBES $215.00
DECEMBER 1936

NC-80X, NC-81X
SIMPLIFIED NC-100X
and 101X
SEPTEMBER 1937 ▷

NC-100XA
.54-30MC   11 TUBES
▷ DRESSED-UP NC-100X
JUNE 1938

NHU
27-62MC   12 TUBES ▷
AUGUST 1939

NATIONAL CO. AMATEUR RECEIVERS

NC-44
.55-46MC   7TUBES
$49.50
44:AC-DC
44A:A-C
44B:BATTERY (6T)
OCTOBER 1939

NC-200 (SERIES)
SIX BANDS.   12 TUBES
AUGUST 1940

NC-45
.55-30 MC   8 TUBES
$51.50
45:AC-DC
45A:AC
45B:BATTERY (7T)
JULY 1941

HRO-5TA
BANDSPREAD - COIL VERSION
OF HRO FOR HAM BANDS
5RA IS RACK-MOUNTED
JANUARY 1946

NC - 2 - 40C
.49-30MC   12 TUBES
ADVANCED NC-200
FEBRUARY 1946
ADVANCED NC-200

239

NATIONAL CO. AMATEUR RECEIVERS

NC-46
.55-46MC   10 TUBES ▷
MARCH 1946

HRO5A1
◁ 50-430KC & .48-30MC
12 TUBES
FEBRUARY 1947

HRO-7
50-43KC & .48-30MC
12 TUBES   AUGUST 1947 ▷

NC-57
◁ .55-56MC.   9 TUBES
$89.50   OCTOBER 1947

NC-183
0.54-31MC, PLUS 6 METERS
NS 269   16 TUBES
ADAPTS TO NBFM USING
NFM-83 ADAPTOR
DECEMBER 1947 ▷

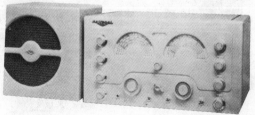

NATIONAL CO. AMATEUR RECEIVERS

NC-33
◊ .5-35MC $65.95
MARCH 1948

NC-173
0.54-31MC & 48-56MC
13 TUBES $179.50
MARCH 1948
◊

HRO-50
◊ 50-43KC & .48-35 MC
14 TUBES $349.00
DECEMBER 1949

241

who but **NATIONAL** builds like this?

Lift the cover of the new NC-125. Look at the sturdy chassis, the quality of the precision-wound coils, the solid construction of the tuning condenser, the dependability of the gear drive. Then remove the bottom plate and examine the cleanness of the cabled wiring. Especially in such a moderate-priced receiver, who but National builds like *this*?

NC-125	$149.50*
NC-125TS (matching spkr.) .	11.00
686S vibrator supply for 6-volt operation	34.16

*Slightly higher west of the Rockies.

Covers 550 kcs. — 36 mcs. in 4 bands. Voice, CW, NFM (with adapter). Edge-lighted, direct-reading scale. Amateur, police, foreign, ship frequencies clearly marked. National Select-O-Ject built-in (rejects any selected audio frequency 45 db — boosts 38 db). Three microvolt sensitivity (for 10 db signal/noise ratio on 10-meter band). S-meter. AVC, ANL, ant. trimmer. Variable CW pitch control. Separate R.F. and audio gain controls. Volt. reg., stabilized oscillator. Jack for phono or NFM Adapter. Audio essentially flat to 10,000 c.p.s.

SEE INSIDE — THEN DECIDE ON

National

NC EST. 1914

NATIONAL COMPANY, Inc.
MALDEN, MASSACHUSETTS

PATTERSON AMATEUR RECEIVERS

◊ PR-10
15-600M   10 TUBES
1934

PR-12
8-550M   12 TUBES
$89.70   DECEMBER 1934 ◊

◊ PR-16
.55-20MC   16 TUBES
DECEMBER 1935

PR-15
7½ - 550M   15 TUBES ◊
$109.50   MAY 1937

RCA AMATEUR RECEIVERS

AR-60
WOOD (SHOWN) $495.00
METAL $485.00
RACK $475.00
NOVEMBER 1935

ACR-175
5-600M.   11 TUBES
APRIL 1936

ACR-55
.55-22MC   9 TUBES
$74.50   FEBRUARY 1937

ACR-111
0.54-30MC   16TUBES
$189.50   AUGUST 1937

ACR-155
.52-22MC   9 TUBES
$74.50   AUGUST 1937

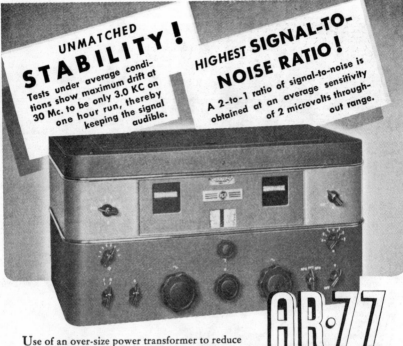

UNMATCHED STABILITY !

Tests under average conditions show maximum drift at 30 Mc. to be only 3.0 KC on one hour run, thereby keeping the signal audible.

HIGHEST SIGNAL-TO-NOISE RATIO !

A 2-to-1 ratio of signal-to-noise is obtained at an average sensitivity of 2 microvolts throughout range.

AR·77

COMMUNICATION RECEIVER

Use of an over-size power transformer to reduce heat; Polystrene insulation at strategic points; a temperature-compensated trimmer that automatically prevents frequency drift, and other RCA features make this new super "tops" in stability of tuning. For instance, during a 60-minute test starting one minute after turning "on", the drift at 30 megacycles was only 3.0 kilocycles. In this same test, when the line voltage was varied from 105 volts to 125 volts the drift at 30 Mc. was only 1300 *cycles*. Match this performance if you can!

As for sensitivity—well, the AR-77 has the highest signal-to-noise ratio of any receiver made by RCA, and that's saying plenty.

These features are typical of the superiority that has been built into *every* electrical and mechanical characteristic of this new receiver. In it, RCA engineering has gone the limit in providing the most exacting performance at a moderate price. Try it at your nearest RCA distributor's store. You be the judge !

Complete Technical Bulletin on request.

Frequency coverage, 540–31,000 KC in *six* Ranges—dual R-F alignment; stay-put tuning; negative feedback in audio amplifier; uni-view dial; calibrated bandspread for 10, 20, 40 and 80 meter bands; accurate signal reset; variable selectivity in six steps with crystal filter; improved image rejection; *adjustable* noise limiter and many other features.

Net Price, **$139.50** *f. o. b. factory. 8" Speaker in matched cabinet,* **$8.00.**

RCA *for Amateur Radio*

RCA MANUFACTURING COMPANY, INC., CAMDEN, N. J. • A Service of the Radio Corporation of America

246

RME AMATEUR RECEIVERS

RME-9
SINGLE—SIGNAL SUPER
.54-22MC.
MAY 1934

RME-69
SINGLE—SIGNAL SUPER
.55-44MC.   9 TUBES
$134.90   DECEMBER 1935

RME-84
.54-44MC   8 TUBES
AC/BATT/6VDC
SEPTEMBER 1947

RME-99
.55-44MC.   12 TUBES
AUGUST 1940

PRECONDITIONERS:
Signal Intensifier
    .55-32MC. October 1936
DM-36 Expander
    "Ultra Short Wave" January 1941
DB22A Preselector
    .54-44MC. September 1947
VHF-152 Converter
    2, 6, 10, 11M September 1947
HF 10-20 Converter
    10, 11, 15, 20M December 1947

VARIOUS AMATEUR RECEIVERS

BRETING 12
.5-30MC   12 TUBES
1935

BRETING 14
.5-30MC   14 TUBES
1937

DE FOREST SHORT-WAVE
20-200M   4 TUBES
JUNE 1930

ECHOPHONE EC-2
.55-30MC   7 TUBES + BALLAST
$29.95   1941
(EC-1, 6 TUBES ALSO
AVAILABLE, $24.50)

ECHOPHONE EC-3
.55-30MC   8 TUBES + BALLAST
$59.50   1941

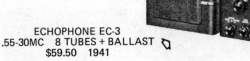

VARIOUS AMATEUR RECEIVERS

GON-SET CO.
STANDARD MOBILE CONVERTER
1947: 20, 15, 10-11, or 6M
1950: 75, 20, 15, 10-11 or 6M
4 TUBES $39.95, NOISE SILENCER $8.25

GON-SET CO.
"3-30" MOBILE CONVERTER ◊
3-30MC $39.95
1950

◊ HOWARD RADIO CO.
HOWARD 430
.54-40MC   6 TUBES
JULY 1938

HOWARD 490
.54-43MC   14 TUBES ◊
SEPTEMBER 1940

HOWARD 435A
.55-43MC   7 TUBES
◊ $34.95   FALL 1941
ALSO:
    436A 8T $39.95
    437A 9T $59.50

GOLDEN-LEUTZ
MODEL 8   ◊
1931

249

VARIOUS AMATEUR RECEIVERS

CANADIAN MARCONI CO.
MARCONI CSR-2
1.5-22MC   MARCH 1936 ◊

◊ MEISSNER MANUF. CO.
TRAFFIC MASTER
14 TUBES   AUGUST 1938

MEISSNER MANUF. CO.
TRAFFIC SCOUT
8 TUBES   AUGUST 1938 ◊

◊ McMURDO-SILVER
SILVER SINGLE-SIGNAL SUPER 5A
1.5-25MC.   SEPTEMBER 1933

NORDEN-HAUCK
SUPER DX-5 ◊
20-200M   6 TUBES
OCTOBER 1930

VARIOUS AMATEUR RECEIVERS

PANDRAMIC RADIO CORP.
PANADAPTOR PCA-2
PANDRAMIC ADAPTOR
$99.75   AUGUST 1939

PILOT RADIO & TELEVISION CO.
PILOT SUPER WASP KIT
$29.50 BATT'Y $34.50 AC
(PLUS POWER PACK)
1927

RADIO ENGINEERING LAB'S, INC.
ALL-PURPOSE RECEIVER
11-1000 METERS   4 TUBES
$36.70   MAY 1931

REC 278
20, 40 & 80M   3 TUBES
$45.00   NOVEMBER 1931

E. M. SARGENT CO.
SARGENT 8-35 ALL-WAVE
15-550M
$49.50   DECEMBER 1934
(Marine Version 15-1500M,
$57.50)

VARIOUS AMATEUR RECEIVERS

◊ SCOTT RADIO LABS
SCOTT SPECIAL
140Kc-64Mc
1940

SHORT WAVE & TELEV. LABS ◊
SHORT WAVE RECEIVER
5 TUBES   JUNE 1930

◊ WIRELESS EGERT
ENGRG. INC.
S-W FOUR KIT
4 TUBES   JUNE 1930

RADIO NEWS, JULY 1930   C. R. LEUTZ, INC.

A NEW POWERFUL
SHORT WAVE RADIO

BY
LEUTZ

AMATEUR TRANSMITTERS

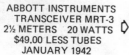 ◊ ABBOTT INSTRUMENTS
TRANSCEIVER DK-3
2½ METERS   2 TUBES
$29.50 LESS TUBES
APRIL 1941

ABBOTT INSTRUMENTS
TRANSCEIVER MRT-3
2½ METERS   20 WATTS ◊
$49.00 LESS TUBES
JANUARY 1942

ABBOTT INSTRUMENTS
◊ TRANSMITTER-RECEIVER TR-4
2½ METERS
$65.00 LESS TUBES
JANUARY 1942

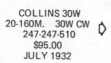

COLLINS 30W
20-160M.   30W CW ◊
247-247-510
$95.00
JULY 1932

AMATEUR TRANSMITTERS

COLLINS 32 A
25W CW, XTAL CONTROL ▷
APRIL 1933

◁ COLLINS 32 B
25W CW, 20W PHONE
XTAL CONTROL
APRIL 1933

⌂
COLLINS 30 FX
100W CW, 40W
PHONE R-F OUTPUT
DECEMBER 1934

◁ COLLINS 30 FCX
175W PHONE /CW
R-F OUTPUT
JANUARY 1936

Collins Transmitter TYPE 40B

The 40B is a high grade phone and CW transmitter embodying the most advanced technical refinements. Its performance, construction, and appearance are not equalled in transmitters selling for many times its price.

100% Class B modulation
25 to 30 watts carrier output

Type 5A
Microphone

Type 90C Amplifier

Type 40B Transmitter

Specifications

Frequency Range: 14,300 to 1,715 kc. Coils for one amateur band are standard equipment.

Modulation: Perfected Class B. The COLLINS 9C Modulator Unit is employed using two 46's Class B driven by two 45's Class A with 82 rectifier. This Unit provides more undistorted modulation power than two 211's Class A with 1,000 volts on the plate.

Fidelity: Flat within 2 db. from 80 to 8,000 cycles. Harmonic content less than 5%. Harshness, caused by transient oscillations present in most Class B systems, is entirely eliminated by means of special circuit and transformers. Each Transmitter is tested with special audio oscillators and cathode ray oscillograph.

R. F. Circuit: The R.F. section of the 40B is identical with the COLLINS 30W. 10A Crystal Control Unit with 247 oscillator, 247 buffer and 510 amplifier is driven by heavy duty power unit. Grid-block keying.

Construction: Burnished aluminum and nickeled chassis mounted on standard 19-inch relay rack. Engraved Formica panels. Surface type Weston meters. Highest quality material throughout. The 40B Transmitter is obtainable either in 34-inch table rack (as illustrated) or in a 60-inch floor rack at no increase in cost.

90C Input Amplifier: Provides necessary gain for operating the 40B with condenser or carbon microphone. Uses two 56's. 500-ohm line to Transmitter.

A complete C.W.-phone installation is priced as follows:

40B Transmitter	$235.00
90C Input Amplifier	32.00
Kit of Matched Tubes	25.75
Crystal and Holder	7.50
5A Condenser Microphone	125.00

F.O.B. CEDAR RAPIDS

Send 25c in coin for manual describing COLLINS Transmitters with parts lists and circuit diagrams

Collins Radio Transmitters
Cedar Rapids, Iowa
W9CXX

AMATEUR TRANSMITTERS

COLLINS 32G
25W20-160M, LESS ON 10M
⇦ OCTOBER, 1936

COLLINS 32RA
50W CW 40W PHONE
1.5-15MC
MAY 1938
⇩

⇦ COLLINS 310B-1
EXCITER TRANSMITTER
10-160M 15W OUTPUT
AUGUST 1947

⇧ COLLINS 30K
500W CW 375W PHONE
5 BANDS   JUNE 1946

⇦ COLLINS 310 C-2
EXCITER 3.2-4 MC
160MW OUTPUT
AUGUST 1947

ELECTRO-MECHANICAL MFG. CO.
⇦ VX-101 DELUXE VFO-CRYSTAL
EXCITER-TRANSMITTER
80-10M, 20-15W. OUT.
$118.50   DECEMBER 1947

AMATEUR TRANSMITTERS

HALLICRAFTERS HT-1
100W CW, 50W PHONE
(HT-2 is CW ONLY) ◊
AUGUST 1938

HALLICRAFTERS HT-4
◊ 10-160M, 450W CW, 325W PHONE
WITH PRE-AMPLIFIER SHOWN
$695.00   NOVEMBER 1939

HALLICRAFTERS
HT-19 NBFM/CW
VFO or XTAL, 3.5-30MC ◊
$298.00   OCTOBER 1948

◊ HARVEY FT-30
APRIL 1935

HARVEY WELLS TBS-50
(BECAME THE BANDMASTER ◊
SERIES) 2-80M, 50W,
$99.50   DECEMBER 1947

AMATEUR TRANSMITTERS

E. F. JOHNSON VIKING I
10-80M, 115W CW, 100W AM
$209.50   SEPTEMBER 1950

RCA ACT-20
10-160M
20W CW, 16W PHONE
$129.50   AUGUST 1937

RCA ACT-200
260W OUTPUT CW
200W OUTPUT PHONE
JANUARY 1936

RADIO ENGINEERING LABS
REL-215. 10W CW
227-224-245. $56.00
MODULATOR AVAILABLE $42.00
OCTOBER 1930

RADIO MANUFACTURING ENGRG.
RME 5-T5.   400W
JANUARY 1936

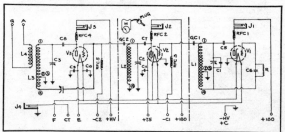
259

AMATEUR TRANSMITTERS

TRANSMITTER EQUIPMENT MFG. CO.
TEMCO 1000
1KW.   JANUARY 1937

TEMCO 75GA1
100W CW   75W PHONE
JUNE 1946

TEMCO RA
MODULAR SERIES
UP TO 250W
CW/AM/FM
JULY 1947

WORLD RADIO
GLOBE KINE
10-80M.   275W PHONE/CW
$399.45   DECEMBER 1948

261

Everyone pitched in during the dark days of World War II.

CHAPTER V
WORLD WAR II RADIO-ELECTRONICS

World War II is a very important part of 1930 to 1950 radio-electronics history. Also, much of the growth of peacetime radio and electronics was spawned by military needs. Let's trace the progress of some of the key military programs.

Military leaders saw the great possibilities of radio in its earliest days in the late 1800's. Many people were introduced to radio (called "wireless" then) by the U. S. Navy's Great White Fleet in the early 1900's. The first World War saw great effort by all the military powers to develop good battlefield radio communications. In fact, E. H. Armstrong was in the Army, working on Army projects, when he invented the tremendously important superheterodyne receiver.

World War II was perhaps the greatest hour for military radio communications and electronics. Radio equipment was a very dependable workhorse. Radar and sonar opened up the detection of aircraft, ships, and submarines at night and in all kinds of weather. No longer did we have to see the enemy in order to accurately fire our guns. Radar worked so well that opposing sides had to develop radar countermeasures and even counter-countermeasures. This was probably the most sophisticated "game" played during that entire conflict. Proximity fuses were another technical accomplishment that affected the course of World War II. Fantastically accurate navigation systems were developed, most notably loran and shoran. Electronic intelligence became an important tool.

Outside of military equipment, electronics were relatively primitive up through the war period, being used mostly to mechanize simple tasks formerly performed by people. In this chapter, we devote ourselves almost entirely to World War II. Although the Korean conflict was in full swing by 1950, most military operations were conducted using warmed-over World War II designs.

RCA AND U.S. NAVY PHOTOS

LONG-RANGE AID TO NAVIGATION (LORAN)

IDENTIFICATION FRIEND-FOE (IFF)

SC-2 AIR SEARCH RADAR

SG-I SURFACE RADAR

MARK IV "FD" FIRE-CONTROL RADAR

TBS VHF TR-REC.

DP DIRECTION FINDER

RAA LO-F REC.

RBA/B/C REC.

TBL

TBK TRANSMITTERS

TDE

RAK-RAL REC.

538

Author's wartime home: Destroyer U.S.S. Stephen Potter and typical World War II shipboard equipment

264

Our radio amateur friends will recognize much of this equipment since many served in the Armed Services, and many more adapted surplus military equipment to Ham communications after the war. Also, many of the military radios were ham sets adapted to military service.

A word of explanation will help. By "radio communications" we mean the wireless transfer of information by voice, code, teletype, or facsimile. "Radar" is radio detection and ranging, the bouncing of high-frequency radio pulses off of objects, measuring the time it takes to get an echo back (hence distance) and antenna position (hence direction). "Sonar" is similar to radar, but is underwater detection and ranging, using ultrasonic sound vibrations. "Loran" (and its cousin "Shoran") is used to find your position on the earth very accurately by measuring the time delays of radio signals from special transmitting stations. "Countermeasures" is where you try to foul up the enemy's communications and electronics by sending out your own deceptive signals. "Elint", electronics intelligence, is analyzing the enemy's radio signals to figure out what he's up to. With a "proximity fuse" a shell can sense when it is near a target and explode itself, so that a direct hit is not required.

Don Elliott, Colonel, U. S. Army, Retired, has had a career that is interwoven with the progress of electronics through the years of this book. He kindly consented to write the following section. Since we can't write all about everything in one chapter, Colonel Elliott has chosen to discuss some typical hardware in field communications, radar and proximity fuzes.

RADIO COMMUNICATIONS

Between World War I and World War II the Army and Navy found themselves in like situations. They tasted first-hand the tremendous tactical value of wireless communications on and over the battlefield and in fleet combat operations, as well as the strategic value of instant contact between the seat of government and far-flung military forces. Both parties were anxious to build upon this knowledge and equip themselves with up-to-date circuits and techniques developed from WW I research.

Where normally they could look to any industry to come forward with the latest equipment having military application, the

BIG: Early World War II portable radio set is typical of a family that started before World War I.

LITTLE: Weighing under five pounds, the SCR-536 was developed by Motorola and went into production in July, 1941. Almost 40,000 were built.

situation regarding communications took a different turn. For one thing, appropriations were meager, allowing little or nothing with which to interest the radio industry in designing equipment with a purely military value. Without the promise of worthwhile contracts for quantity production, most manufacturers preferred joining in the broadcast radio "boom" sweeping the country. Consequently, both services eventually organized and manned their own laboratories where basic research, development and prototype manufacture took place. Thus fostered, the most promising designs were either constructed entirely within the military establishment, shelved for future consideration, or built in limited quantities by a few enterprising and far-sighted companies. Even with adequate funding, it is questionable whether the situation would have been different when we realize that the usual government contract placed liability for possible patent infringement upon the manufacturer, this precaution alone discouraged most manufacturers from risking their financial health in an era that saw tremendous court battles taking place between the presumed holders of the basic circuits and components upon which the advanced equipment designs were dependent.

In any event, the late '20's and '30's saw the basic structuring of military communications as the planners would like to have it, but sans equipment to do the planned job until early 1941. By then it was almost too late. Yet, in the five years that followed, the military establishment succeeded in building and operating the most efficient and extensive communication complex known to any military force in history. Let's take a brief look at the equipment and organization. To begin with, the hallmark of military radio equipment was reliability, ruggedness and simplicity of operation. The requirement for reliability was two-fold; not only was it necessary that the equipment do its task as designed, but that downtime be kept to a minimum and for prescribed maintenance only. Such standards, when met, would reduce the kind and number of spare parts required in overseas depots and in the "supply pipe-line" between manufacturer and equipment location. Ruggedness on the other hand was the design and construction feature necessary for reliable operation under combat and adverse conditions. For example, equipment intended for an infantry regiment had to operate equally well in the jungle, de-

MILITARY RADIO

R-80 Receiver, showing design changes made on Hallicrafters S-29 Sky Ranger for military use. Used for troop information and entertainment. 9 tubes. AC-DC-BATT.

TWO CONFIGURATIONS
OF SCR-506

TRANSMITTER-
RECEIVER
USED IN TANKS
AMPHIBIAN TRUCKS
AND
PERSONNEL
CARRIERS

SCR-506 CONSISTS
OF BC-652A RADIO RECEIVER
AND BC-653A TRANSMITTER
PLUS POWER SUPPLY
AND HARDWARE.

SCR-506 was the faithful work-horse of mobile units. 50-90 watts. CW output over 4.5-2.0 Mc range, 15-25 watts phone. Developed in 1940-41.

sert or artic. In addition to obvious external strength, the chassis wiring and quality of components, together with anti-fungus and humidity treatment throughout, permitted a level of ruggedness adequate for pure military designs. Finally, simplicity of operation was essential in light of the training requirement imposed at operator schools and, more important, the stress situations under which the combat operator might find himself.

An interesting feature of military radio intended for field or shipboard use was the intentional suppression of range. Besides the obvious need to limit transmission range for security reasons, another need arose because of the density of stations within possible mutual interference range of each other. In fact, the first wartime "shortage" was the "spectrum" shortage! Throughout the war years techniques to obtain more efficient use of the radio spectrum resulted in several major breakthroughs such as single-sideband, suppressed-carrier transmission to name just one. Also, "families" of equipment, crystal controlled to pre-assigned "pushbutton" frequencies permitted inter-unit communication nets that provided maximum flexibility and utility at the minimum expense of required frequencies.

A typical field radio set embodying the military features thus far described was the Army SCR-506 medium range mobile radio set. Designed under the auspices of the Fort Monmouth Signal Laboratories by the General Electric Company, it embodied all of the desirable features thought necessary by the Armored Force and Cavalry. In a space of 14 x 14 x 34 inches the prototype SCR-506 contained an eight-tube superhetrodyne receiver, a quick frequency shift transmitter capable of from 50 to 90 watts output from 4500 to 2500 Kc. CW (code only) and power supplies for both units. It was found desirable to add AM voice modulation for air-to-ground communications. The additional feature was built within the existing transmitter cabinet for all production models. Four pre-set and one tunable transmitting frequency bands were furnished, any of which could be selected by single switch action. Altogether, within the frequency range from 2000 to 4500 Kc, 125 preset frequencies could be chosen. Completely sealed, both receiver and transmitter were forced-air cooled. The receiver was required to operate up to 8 hours continuously under conditions of 90 percent

SCR-195 (infantry) and SCR-194 (field artillery) were the first Walkie-Talkies, brought out in 1936. SCR-195 is shown.

SCR-511, designed for cavalry in 1940, was the only light Walkie-Talkie when **WW II** broke out, and saw wide use by infantry.

SCR-300 (AN/VRC-3 for tanks) came out in 1942 and was the Infantry Walkie-Talkie during most of **WW II**. Also saw service in Korea.

SCR-509/510/609/610 was used by cavalry and armor during early war years.

SCR-619 phased out SCR-609 starting in 1944, since 609 was too heavy to really operate "Walkie-Talkie."

U. S. Army Radio Central Control AN/TRQ-1.

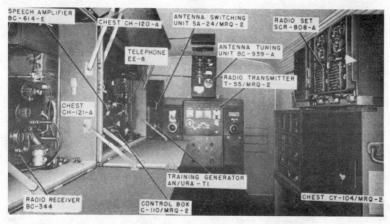

Radio set AN/MRQ-2, companion to AN/TRQ-1

271

WORLD WAR II
MILITARY RADIO

◊ AN/SRR-3 RECEIVER, AM-CW
SCOTT MODEL SLR-F, A-C,
FOR SHIP AND SHORE USE.

AN/VRC-3
FM TRANSMITTER-RECEIVER ◊
(BASICALLY SCR-300
WITH MOUNTING BRACKETS)
BATTERY POWERED.

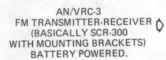

◆ BC-312 RECEIVER AM-CW
12 VERSIONS
VEHICLE, PORTABLE OR FIXED.

BC-610 TRANSMITTER
WITH BC-939 ANTENNA ◊
TUNER. SIX VERSIONS.

WORLD WAR II
MILITARY RADIO

BC-779 RECEIVER, AM-CW
A & B VERSIONS PLUS
R-129U, ALL WITH
DIFFERENT FREQ'S.
HAMMARLUND SUPER-PRO.

BC-787 B RECEIVER, AM-FM-CW
27.8-143Mc

R-100/URR "MORALE
BUILDER" FOR TROOP
INFORMATION AND
ENTERTAINMENT
AC-DC-BATT

R-211/U RECEIVER
AND POWER SUPPLY
9 TUBES.   NATIONAL HRO

RE-1 SEMIPORTABLE RADIO
FOR TROOP INFORMATION
AND ENTERTAINMENT.
AC-DC-BATT.
HALLICRAFTERS
SKY COURIER

273

WORLD WAR II MILITARY RADIO

◊ SCR-508 FM COMBAT
VEHICLE RADIO
BC-604 TRANSMITTER
BC-603 RECEIVER
SIX VERSIONS

SCR-543
MEDIUM-RANGE ◊
COMM SET
A,B,C VERSIONS

◊ SCR-619, VEHICULAR
VERSION WITH BATTERY
CHARGER. 6, 12 or 24V

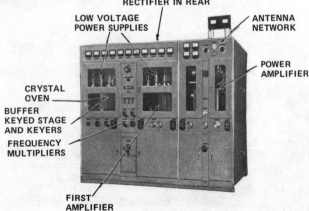

HIGH VOLTAGE
RECTIFIER IN REAR

LOW VOLTAGE
POWER SUPPLIES

ANTENNA
NETWORK

POWER
AMPLIFIER

CRYSTAL
OVEN

BUFFER
KEYED STAGE
AND KEYERS

FREQUENCY
MULTIPLIERS

FIRST
AMPLIFIER

T-172/FR TRANSMITTER
CW to 350 WPM.

274

AIRCRAFT RADIO EQUIPMENT

CONTROL
BOXES

TUNING
HEAD

MODEL ARB NAVY RECEIVER

BC-224 RECEIVER

RCVRS: BC-453/4/5-A
XMTRS: BC-457/8-A
WITH MODULATOR/POWER UNIT.

SCR-274-N ARMY AIR FORCE COMMAND
SET, 190KC to 9.0MC.

The Collins-designed transmitter as the operator sees it from his station in a Superfortress. Boeing—Wichita Photo.

Superfortresses blast and roast the Japs. Official photo U. S. A. A. F.

In the Boeing B-29 from the first

THE FIRST MESSAGE from the Army's first Boeing Superfortresses over Japan, on the Yawata mission of June 15, 1944, was transmitted by a Collins radio transmitter of the type shown above. From that time on, this transmitter has been standard equipment for all the Superforts, as it is also for the larger Naval aircraft.

As the Army and Navy demand increased, requirements exceeded the capacity of the extensive Collins facilities, and other manufacturers of radio equipment were drawn into the production program, aided by Collins engineers. Total deliveries have been very large.

Collins engineering and production have gained much valuable experience during the war in providing reliable radio communications under all operating conditions in practically every quarter of the globe. This experience will be available to commercial and personal users as soon as military requirements permit. Collins Radio Company, Cedar Rapids, Iowa; 11 West 42nd Street, New York 18, N. Y.

IN RADIO COMMUNICATIONS, IT'S . . .

AN/ART-13 (Navy ATC-1)
100W output AM-CW-MCW
2-18.1 MC, 200-1500 KC with adaptors

THE NAVY

The Navy uses many kinds of communications for guiding ships and in maintaining contact with members of our fleet and the many other branches of our services.

Typical radio installation on large Navy aircraft.

First shipboard radar – U. S. Naval research laboratory experimental equipment on U.S.S. Leary, April 1937. Antenna is mounted on gun barrel.

First operational Army radar: SCR-268. This radar detected approaching Japanese planes on December 7, 1941.

278

humidity at an ambient temperature of 122°F. The transmitter was required to remain on frequency within 0.05 percent (1000 cycles at 2000 Kc, for example) with variations of temperature ranging between −22°F to 131°F. All connections between units and their power supplies and to the external vehicle battery were made via the slide connectors fastening the equipment to the mounting base. The antenna was a 15 foot 5-section whip. Mounted in its protective case the SCR-506 weighed 223.5 pounds (75 pounds heavier than originally designed because all aluminum had been eliminated from its construction). Altogether, this was an outstanding set that saw service in all theaters of military operation.

On the other hand, fixed station, high-powered transmitters and receivers intended for continental and trans-oceanic communications paralleled commercial practice and, except for certain applications, comprised "off-the-shelf" equipments found in most commercial stations. Hand-keying and speed-tape equipment soon gave way to an overall system using high-speed radio teletype plus advanced radio telephone techniques between the Pentagon and major overseas headquarters.

Airborne radio was originally in the HF portion of the spectrum (below 30Mc) but later followed British RAF equipment design operating in the VHF portion of the radio spectrum (30 to 300 Mc) with its resultant adoption by commercial airline operations.

The equipments shown in this book represent the barest cross-section of the literally hundreds of individual transmitters, receivers, radio sets and fixed station installations that saw service in the armed forces.

RADAR

The pressure of war saw the expansion of the radio industry into fields far removed from communications. Of these, radar is probably the development having the greatest interest to the general reader. Having discussed the technical detail elsewhere, it is appropriate here to outline a few examples of how radar was employed.

The Navy used radar in three basic ways: Surface search or surveillance, air search, and fire control. The surface search role

XAF radar, Navy's only operational radar at opening of World War II. Antenna was a wire mesh in the frame shown in the right hand photo on U.S.S. New York in 1938.

had an application in convoy and fleet operations. Such groupings of vessels require strict station-keeping on the part of all vessels. Evasive maneuvers on the part of the whole require complex and everchanging maneuvers by each ship. To so maneuver at night, in fog, or when under enemy fire is most difficult. Surface search radar permitted the convoy or fleet commander as well as individual ship captains to know with exactness the location and movement of all vessels regardless of visability limitations. It would be difficult to calculate the number of merchantmen that would not have reached port if not so equipped.

Air search radar, as the name implies, was a form of early-warning radar to alert air-defense artillery and interceptors to the approach of aircraft at distances sufficient to prepare defensive operations. In addition to presenting the air situation to the commanders concerned, it was capable of transferring the bearing, elevation, and range of incoming aircraft to the fire-control radar for the more precise tracking needed for gun-laying computations. Generally speaking, search radars utilized PPI, or plan position indicator, scope presentations for an overall mapping the air space surrounding the fleet in a manner similar to the mapping presented by the surface search radars.

Fire control radar, on the other hand, was concerned with precise tracking of individual aircraft or formations against which it was intended to engage. Consequently, it employed a narrow pencil beam "locked" onto the aircraft in question so as to follow its every maneuver. Such "present position" data, fed into fire control computers, resulted in calculating the bearing, elevation and fuzing data needed by the anti-aircraft guns to engage the aircraft.

Army radar development closely paralleled that of the Navy except there was no particular need for surface-search equipment. In Army parlance, "early warning" radars performed the "air-search" function and fed data to "target tracking" radars for fire control processing. Also, because the basic tactical anti-aircraft artillery unit was a semi-mobile battery of four guns, each battery had its own early-warning radar van-mounted so as to accompany the battery in the field. Linked together with radio and wire communication nets the early-warning radars served a dual function; providing data for their own batteries,

SG surface radar, work-horse of the combat fleet. Left is "A" scope for measuring range; center is compass repeater showing ship's heading and target direction (bearing); right is PPI scope giving a "map" of surrounding features. 3,000 Mc. Smaller version was the SO radar.

SC-2 air search radar for early warning of enemy air attack and for controlling friendly planes. 200-250 Mc. Larger version on aircraft carriers and battleships was the SK radar.

MIRACLE TUBES OF RADAR

Magnetron tube delivers hundreds of kilowatts of microwave -frequency pulse power in radar transmitters.

Reflex klystron delivers continous microwave energy for local oscillations in radar receivers. This particular one operates at 3,000 mc.

Metal tube is a reflex klystron for radar L. O. use at 9,000 mc. Glass tube is a duplexer, which acts as a switch to keep transmitter pulse from burning out the receiver.

as well as contributing to the overall early-warning function of the Corps or Army air-defense control centers established by the senior field headquarters.

The Army's SCR-268 and Navy's XAF radars did yeoman service during the early months of the conflict. It was an SCR-268 overlooking the approaches to Hawaii that observed the attacking Japanese aircraft on December 7, 1941. Manned by personnel who would otherwise have been off duty except for a training exercise, their report of sighting many approaching and ――to them――unknown aircraft was disregarded until too late.

Radar became a truly effective device when the magnetron became available. Originally developed by the British it allowed their radar systems to turn the tide during the Battle of Britain. Observing the German formations grouping over northern France for their massed bombing, the radars provided timely warning to alert the fighter squadrons to the impending attacks.

Arrangements were made for the Americans to copy and manufacture the special device and, during the war years, continued improvements were made in its performance. For one example: the external permanent magnet associated with the ground-based magnetron weighed between 10 and 40 pounds depending on its function. One magnetron chosen for an aircraft application weighed 17 pounds until redesigned to have the magnet internal to the tube construction, with a resultant all-up weight of 3½ pounds with no sacrifice in efficiency or mechanical characteristics. For a final example, where early magnetrons delivered peak powers of 80 to 100 Kilowatts at about 20 percent efficiency, a later model, type 4J31, could deliver 1 megawatt at about 50 percent efficiency. There is no question that radar, because of the magnetron, was THE electronic marvel of WW II.

PROXIMITY FUSE

A close second to radar would have to be the anti-aircraft artillery proximity fuse. Conceived by the Navy and developed by John Hopkins University at the Applied Physics Laboratory, it found its place in history first in the Pacific theater where, for security reasons, its use was restricted over water to preclude the enemy finding out its existence and, finally, in the Battle of the Bulge, where it was adapted to field artillery use with devastating results.

Its operation was deceptively simple: A small internal transmitter would send a radio wave ahead which, upon striking the enemy aircraft could be reflected back to the fused projectile. As the projectile moved toward the aircraft the strength of the returned radio energy increased until finally it, plus a sampled portion of the transmitted energy, was sufficiently large to operate a thyratron switching tube. This, in turn, closed the circuit permitting a charged capacitor to discharge through the ignitor train of the fuse itself, setting off the projectile.

THE PROXIMITY FUSE

RADIO NEWS, DECEMBER 1945

500-POUND BOMB
WITH PROXIMITY FUSE

Containing a five-tube radio sending and receiving set, this fuse explodes a projectile as soon as it comes close enough to a target to inflict damage.

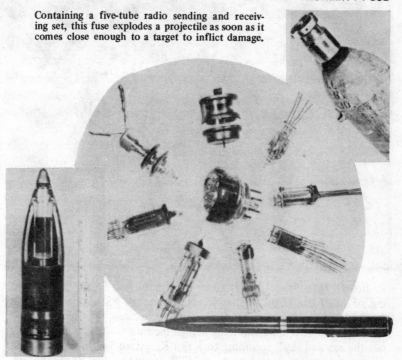

5-INCH SHELL
WITH PROXIMITY FUSE
(CUTAWAY DISPLAY)

RUGGEDIZED TUBES DEVELOPED
FOR
PROXIMITY FUSE USE.

Radioman John Stannage was a key man on the first East-West air crossing of the Atlantic by Charles Kingsford-Smith's "Southern Cross" in
1930. All navigation was by radio bearings because "The clouds thick-
ened up mile after mile, climbing in high mountains ahead of us, blotting
out the sea and sky" according to Major Kingsford-Smith. Stannage and
other radiomen, such as Amory "Bud" Waite of Admiral Byrd's Antarctic expeditions, enhanced the fine tradition of all radiomen.

CHAPTER VI
THE RADIOMAN

Radiomen, (actually both men and women) are the ones who keep radio communications running, almost in partnership with the electronic machines over which they are masters. Oldest in this line is the ship to shore radio operator, since this was the first use of radio equipment. Shipboard radio operators probably had the best of lives in the world of radio, combining travel and adventure with the great feeling of responsibility and accomplishment. Many a youngster had dreamed of a romantic life on the high seas, surrounded by mag· ificent radio equipment, tapping out messages of vital importance to his fellow adventurers on the seas or shore. This dream came to life for a lucky few.

Radiomen have participated in many great adventures. Jack Binns sent the first distress call in 1906 as his ship was rammed and sinking. John Stannage was a key man on Charles Kingsford-Smith's crew of the airplane "Southern Cross" as it made history's first East-West crossing of the Atlantic in 1930. Amory "Bud" Waite was admiral Byrd's radioman on most of his Antarctic expeditions. Many a radioman braved the dangers of land, sea and air during wartime, and more than a few did not come home again. No matter what the radio operator's ship, aircraft or station, there was always the chance that an emergency would plunge him into the middle of a life-and-death drama. This is part of what attracted such a special breed of adventurer into life as a radioman.

Some of us recall the roll of a ship as it pushed its way through the water to far-away places. We remember not only the sounds and smells of the ship, but the far-away ports which had their own unique character and yet somehow seemed much the same. Old hands can tell you that it wasn't all fun and romance. They recall storms which were at least uncomfortable and may even have required the barf bucket by the operating position. Only a few were aboard fancy passenger ships; most were radio men aboard freighters plying their way up and down

Master of His Domain

"On board" the radio operator is recognized an an officer of his ship with almost as much responsibility for his passengers as the captain. In his cabin, surrounded by complicated radio apparatus of all varieties, he is supreme. Every soul aboard relies on him for contact with the outside world, for weather reports, storm warnings, news and emergency messages. This is the radio cabin of the Discovery II.

the coast or across the world. There were many adventures with strange cargoes, especially if the load started to shift as the ship heaved in stormy seas. Many a "brass-pounder" remembers the terrible smell of some unsavory cargoes, or the all-pervading grime from a load of creosoted logs. He can also recall those long terrible dull hours of the midwatch, when the only thing between him and that much-welcomed but forbidden sleep was a mug of hot coffee clutched in his hand.

In case of emergency, the radioman rocketed to supreme importance. He handled traffic vital for the survival of ships and of men floundering in the seas. The radioman was committed to stay at his station until his transmitter could no longer transmit. This duty had a romantic ring, but assumed terrible weight when the ship might go down.

All in all, the radioman had a good life, and most ex-operators recall it with a great deal of pleasure and some longing for those old days.

In the 1930's, the blandishments of radio schools could hardly be ignored by depression-hungry youngsters looking for interesting and available work. "Win fame and fortune" the ads screamed. "You'll get thrills-adventure." "Opportunity is knocking at your door." Fortunately there was as much truth as fiction in these claims, for the radio industry was growing at a tremendous clip even in hard times, and World War II caused an urgent need for competent radio operators and technicians.

Wartime was something of a frustrating experience for the radio operator aboard ship. Requirements for radio silence meant that he spent most of his time receiving messages, with the privilege of transmitting only on special occasions, perhaps as his mortally-wounded ship sank beneath the waves.

World War II gave rise to a new breed; the radio-electronics technician. This was a new community of bright kids who had responsibility for keeping ever-more complicated radio, radar, sonar, and other electronic equipment running through times of great danger. After the war these technicians moved on into commercial radio and electronics, became engineers, or set up their own service businesses in the complicated world of television.

Many radiomen found their spots as operating engineers in

Seeing the World as a Radio Man

"Ka-WHUMP!" The ship's bow digs into another big one as it plows through black, heaving seas under grey skies. But tomorrow the sun may shine, and your ship may be rocking along over gentle blue swells, You never forget the feel of the sea, or the sights and smells of faraway places like Las Palmas, Kamakura or Rio de Janiero. You may even recall the great misadventure; shipwreck!

radio stations, commercial shore stations and police departments. Every station required a competent, licensed radio operator to be in charge of the radio equipment while on the air. The life of the operating broadcasting engineer consisted of many hours of boredom punctuated by moments of panic as the transmitter emitted a loud "crack", or as the program suddenly dropped off the air. It was at these moments that the engineer had to make sudden decisions in order to get back on the air, even if at quarter-power, and to do some daring gymnastics as he replaced a final amplifier tube right next to a driver tube that was still swinging 2500 volts a million times a second.

One of the mainstays of broadcasting has always been the radio repairman. The radio repairman had to invest heavily in equipment and training and then work at fever pitch to repair enough sets to make a living. At the same time he had to be a great psychologist in order to get his money out of his customers, many of whom considered it something of a contest.

All-in-all the life of a radioman was (and is) a good one. Many men chose to spend their entire lives in this spiritually (if not financially) rewarding business, while others decided to jump into the gut-grinding race to help grow the radio-electronics industry. The best example is David Sarnoff, operator for American Marconi, who made RCA the giant of the radio-television-elec-tronic world, and who founded both the National Broadcasting Company and the American Broadcasting Company. Another radio operator was a young fellow by the name of Arthur Godfrey. The roster of the Society of Wireless Pioneers is replete with the names of the men who led illustrious careers as radiomen, and those who moved on to conquer other worlds. You might say that the radioman (and operating technician these days) is the heart of our radio-television-electronics operating world, while the "Ham" is the reservist.

So now, at least, the radioman has been immortalized just a bit and the world will know a little more about his contributions to progress, service and public well-being.

J.E. Smith, Pres.

Broadcasting stations need trained men.

Television — Great opportunity for trained radio men.

See the world and get good pay plus expenses.

Aviation needs trained radio men. $2,000 to $2,800 a year.

Talking movies offer many fine jobs to trained radio men.

NATIONAL RADIO INSTITUTE

You'll Get *Thrills* · Adventure

RCA PHOTO, 1943

RCA Institute training operators for war assignments in World War II.

What young man could ignore these promises of fame and fortune?

KFI's transmitter, 1930. Operating engineers are responsible for keeping the station on the air, on frequency, with full power and high signal quality, without interruption.

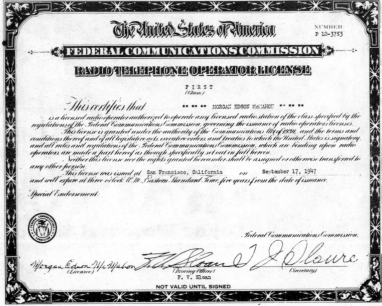

First Class Radio Telephone Operator License, the "ticket" needed to command a broadcasting station's transmitter.

In 1930 radio repair involved batteries, speakers, an array of meters on a home-brew switching panel, and good intuition.

RADIO & TELEVISION RETAILING, MARCH 1940

By 1940 the progressive repairman had a broad array of instruments available, plus Rider's manuals giving circuit diagrams of almost all sets. A good repairman had to be well-schooled in radio theory and test techniques.

Morgan McMahon with wireless, radio and TV ranging from World War
I to 1950. Early sets are becoming scarce. New collectors might best start
with the late 1920's and early 1930's, or with particularly interesting
sets up to 1950. Specialization can follow, and often does, once you
discover what interests you most. Some of us stay general with "mini-
museums" which can be little or big.

CHAPTER VII
COLLECTING

There's no thrill exactly like bumping into a rare old radio set at someone's barn sale, or like finding the Atwater Kent radio that fills a gap in your collection. Radio collecting has something for everybody, but doesn't demand too much from anyone. You can adopt one or two fine old sets as conversation pieces, or you can fill your home with them. You can get as much fun per dollar as you want, and be making a good investment in the bargain.

Collecting wireless, radio and early TV is everybody's ball game. Anyone can play. The name of the game is to keep these pieces of history from being tossed on the junk heap, and to turn them into collectors' items instead. Poke around junque shops. Haunt swap meets. Visit old radio shops. Chase garage sales. Answer ads. Get to know fellow collectors.

We're talking mostly about the years 1900 to 1950, although some far-sighted people are collecting items from later years. The old hard-core-historians, about 500 of them, have rescued many of the artifacts from pre-1920 wireless. There's been quite a bit of activity in collecting old 1920's battery sets. We've just come to realize that sets and memorabilia from the golden years of radio broadcasting (late 1920's to 1950) and early television have historical value. A whole herd of collectors have started thundering down the trail of these latter-day "antiquities."

A radio or TV doesn't have to play to be collectible; it can be what museums like to call a "static display." If it does play, so much the better.

How do you get started as a collector? First, you spot an interesting old radio. You buy, telling yourself that you'll have it just as a conversation piece. Then, (maybe months later) you spot another one and tell yourself that two conversation pieces would be better than just one. You buy. Then you spot a much different set, and you tell yourself how nice it would be to have a variety. You buy. Then you spot a "His Master's Voice" dog, and wouldn't that go great? You buy. Then you see a stack of old Radio News magazines, and aren't they interesting? You buy. By now you're hooked. You come to know some other victims of the same affliction. You start to trade things, because by now you've decided to collect mostly Atwater Kents, or RCA Radiolas, or Zenith portables, or Philco "cathedrals." Maybe you've decided to collect a smattering of everything from 1921 to 1950, and have your own home-grown museum.

Anything and everything about the great radio revolution is collectible. You may want to collect radio parts, especially since they take up less room. For instance, radio tubes make a fascinating and historical collection.

Some people collect headphones, radiotelegraph keys, testers, crystal sets, or magazines. Many people collect records and tapes of old-time radio programs and magazines telling of goings-on among stars like Eddie Cantor, Fannie Brice, Major Bowes and Rudy Vallee. If it's interesting, someone collects it.

If you want to collect wireless equipment you've got a rough row to hoe. It's a trick just to recognize early wireless equipment, let alone find it. Many of the artifacts of the wireless age have already found their way to collectors and museums and aren't available. If you do want to get into wireless collecting get to know a real collector, and read the available literature. There's no firm price structure in wireless hardware, but you can be sure it's not cheap. One word of caution; there are some beautiful replicas, easily mistaken for the real thing.

The radio broadcast era began in 1919, and brought with it a flood of interesting, and sometimes weird, radio sets. You can appreciate the quality of craftsmanship and the array of knobs, dials and switches on the old battery sets of the 1920's. Look at an old console model of the 1930's; you can almost see the family grouped around it, listening to their favorite Sunday afternoon program. Touch an old wooden table-model radio; you can almost hear Franklin D. Roosevelt condemn the December 7, 1941 attack on Pearl Harbor, the "date which will live in infamy." Today you can actually tune in some of the old programs again, if you watch your local radio schedule.

There isn't yet a standard price for vintage radios, but we can give you some general figures. It really comes down to what you're willing to pay and what the guy on the other end is wil-

John Porter has devoted his life and fortune to the preservation of historical radios. His museum of 1400 sets fills the old hotel and jail at Hornbrook, California, and he also has a mobile display van.

ling to take. Location is an important consideration, since it can cost many dollars to ship a large, heavy set across-country. (Incidentally, some carriers are far cheaper than others; check them out first.) Also, you'd expect to pay less at a garage sale than at an antique shop where the legwork has already been done for you. Condition is very important; a set in mint or fully restored condition is worth several times what you'd pay for a restorable hulk.

You can expect to pay $15 to $80 for a typical 1920's battery set, with some models going much higher. Particular early sets can command over $150. An Atwater-Kent "Breadboard" radio may run to $250 or more depending on model and condition.

A Federal receiver will run in the $50-up range, with some as high as $250. Other early battery sets that bring good prices are Grebe, DeForest, Kennedy, Fada, Freed-Eisemann, Freshman, Gilfillan, Paragon, RCA (Aeriola and Radiola), and Zenith. There were about 1,100 set manufacturers in the 1920's, plus many interesting home-builts, so you'll still bump into opportunities to add to your collection.

A-C sets range from under $1 to over $200 depending on model, age, workmanship, styling and condition. Late 1920's and 1930's A-C sets bring around $15 as-is, $45 in good cosmetic shape and $60 in restored, playing condition. Most in demand is the compact, so-called "depression" radio of the early and mid-1930's. In particular, the dome-top and pointed-top "cathedral" model brings top dollar, ranging from $20 as-is to $100 or more restored and playing. Some exceptional sets may bring much more. If you have room, the best buys are in console models. Philco, RCA, Silver-Marshall and Magnavox built very good sets, but the most magnificent were by Zenith and Scott. Incidentally, RCA's sets were actually built by Westinghouse and General Electric in the 1920's.

In the 1930's inexpensive mass-produced radios became popular. High-quality sets were still made for true musical entertainment, but it's the "junker" that really took voice and music into every room of every home. These sets have been the mainstay of radio broadcasting ever since, and deserve a place in our hall of fame. They can be acquired for from one to several dollars,

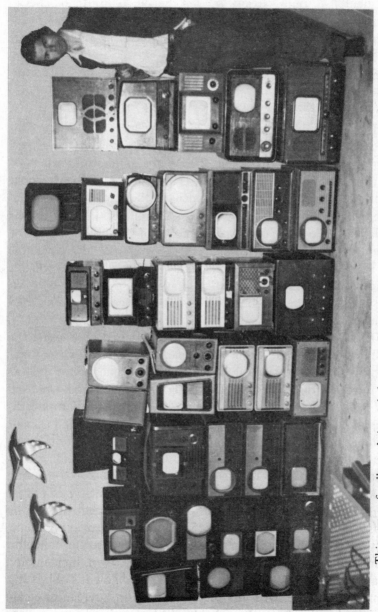

This array of collector's items belongs to Charles A. "Chuck" Seidel of Santa Barbara, California.

yet could make a very interesting collection.

Portable radios have survived the years very well because they were ruggedly built in the first place. You could make a collection of portables on a minimum budget.

Auto radios are an important part of radio history, but they don't make a very beautiful collection. Auto restoration buffs will give their eye teeth for particular sets to fit their particular cars, so auto radios might make a rewarding sideline business for someone.

During World War II civilian radio production was at a minimum because of wartime priorities and shortages. One can almost make a collection of the "make-do" and bootleg sets built during those years. World War II military equipment would make a good collection, but much of the hardware has been junked because of limited civilian usefulness. Radio amateur "Hams" have hung onto many pieces of old military gear for their stations, and might be a good source to the collector.

Television collecting has become popular almost overnight. Prices of some of the earliest sets have gone nearly out of sight. It's hard to lose, though, because the price isn't going anywhere but up.

The earliest TV sets were built in the late 1920's using the primitive flying-spot scanner principle. This set featured a motor-driven wheel with a spiral set of holes in it, making the picture as the holes ran between a flickering light and a small window. TV-tube television, pioneered by Zworykin and Farnsworth, was available in Los Angeles and New York by 1937, and a small number of sets were in operation by 1940. It wasn't until 1946 that television really took off, spurred by radar technology developed in World War II.

Many pre-1951 sets can still be picked up for bargain prices. With luck, a 5, 7 or 10-inch tube set can be bought for $35 in as-is condition, and typically $75 playing and cleaned up. Some sets will go up in value more quickly than others, as the collector community decides which are the "in" sets to own. Incidentally, if a set has provision for Channel One you know it's old. If it's a projection type, with the picture shown on a screen or an aluminized metal sheet it's probably 1951 or earlier.

Old-time radio tubes can be a problem. For a static display, you should have the right tubes in the right sockets even if they don't work. For a playing radio, you have no choice. It will cost you anywhere from $2.50 up for a vintage tube, if you can find it at all. Take this into account when buying a set for your collection.

There are some guidelines in acquiring a vintage set. If the set has been butchered and "modernized" beyond redemption, forget it. If its innards aren't the original ones for which the cabinet was built, forget it. If the cabinet is so far gone you have to rebuild it from scratch, forget it.

How about restoring that fine old radio or TV set? The number one requirement is that its original beauty be restored, possibly enhanced by the years. It's obviously desirable to have the the set playing, but don't scrap a good set just because it's voiceless at the moment.

Let's assume you've just dragged the set out of Aunt Edna's attic. The first thing you do is to use that miracle cleaner known as soap and water. Watch out for modern super cleaners and scouring powders, since they can damage the old finish, dissolve putty knobs and fog plastic windows.

After the bath you can really see what needs to be done; veneer glued or replaced, knobs mended, grille cloth replaced, new dial glass, and so forth.

Remember some basic rules of restoration: It's better to restore old parts than to use new ones. Don't take short cuts in making the set play (the supreme crime is to tear up the chassis and replace it with a transistor radio). Restore the original finish if at all possible, rather than stripping and refinishing.

That last rule is very important. I've seen people ruin fine cabinets by slopping them with varnish stain. I've seen fine finishes stripped and refinished with plastic coatings when all they really needed was three applications of Old English scratch-remover polish and some elbow grease. How about crazed finishes? There are some very good corrective chemicals available at antique and hardware stores, and you can't lose anything by trying. If you have to refinish, try to duplicate the original surface. This may take anything from oil rubs to hard varnish.

Now - how do you get your collector's item working? All the little beauties in your collection don't have to play, but the

303

ones that do will be the gems in your crown. If you're nontechnical, get someone competent (not that self-styled genius next door) to restore the insides. If you know something about radio, the next several paragraphs will help.

Most old radios do not operate after many years in storage. If you plug an A-C set into the socket without checking it out, you run a chance of burning out the power transformer because of shorted filter capacitors (or condensers, as they were called in the old days). Paper dielectric wound condensers are also most likely bad, or will go bad shortly. Sometimes they can be saved by starting at a low voltage and increasing the voltage gradually over a period of days. The remedy for bad condensers is not to replace them with equally old ones that will go bad just as quickly. Rather, we must replace the old insides with new ones, keeping the original appearance.

Transformers are another problem. In the old days, paper insulation contained sulfur, and corrosive solder fluxes were used. The result is that old transformers may fail at any time. The old transformer can be rewound, or a new transformer can be put inside the old case by the nonpurist.

WARNING: Do NOT attempt to hitch up voltage or repair radio or TV sets unless you know what you are doing. You can do irreparable damage to both yourself and the equipment. This is especially true of A-C sets.

Where do you go for information on collecting and restoration? The most useful books are those from Vintage Radio, which has been organized specifically to help the old-time radio-TV-electronics bug. Books presently in VR's bag (besides this one, of course) are Vintage Radio, a pictorical history of radio 1887-1929; Radio Collector's Guide, 1921-1932 a data book with over 50,000 pieces of information, 4,000 set models and 1,100 manufacturers; S. Gernsback's 1927 Radio Encyclopedia, a fascinating detailed review of the people and technology of those times; and M. Beitman's Most-Often-Needed 1927-1938 Radio Diagrams. Information on these books is available from Vintage Radio, Box 2045, Palos Verdes Peninsula, CA, 90274. We'll produce other informative and enjoyable books as fast as we can.

Other good books on broadcasting's history and personalities are available, as discussed in Chapter II.

So now you know all we know about collecting. You can get out there and capture some of those fascinating old beauties for yourself. You'll come to know the thrill of the chase, the joy of discovery and the pride of ownership.

GOOD HUNTING !

CHAPTER VIII
HOW IT WORKS

HOW IT WORKS

The inner workings of radios are a great mystery to most of us. This chapter will help you understand the circuit names that are tossed around by the "experts". At least you won't feel like a dummy!

CRYSTAL SETS

Some of the early sets didn't have tubes in them. The radio-frequency signal was changed into an audio-frequency signal, which drove the earphones, using a crystal detector. Crystal detectors are made of a crystal of material, such as galena, iron pyrites, or silicon. Many of us built crystal sets as kids, and kits are still available. Today's sets often use pre-assembled germanium crystal detectors.

"ONE TUBERS"

In old one-tube sets, a vacuum tube was used as the detector. It had the advantage of amplifying while it detected, making weak signals strong and even getting loudspeaker volume on some stations. Most one-tube sets used "regeneration" in which amplified energy was fed back into the input to be amplified again. This gave very good amplification of weak signals at the cost of squeaks and squawks.

"TWO-TUBERS"

Two-tubers used a detector tube and an audio amplifier tube, giving a good strong signal for phones or low-power speakers.

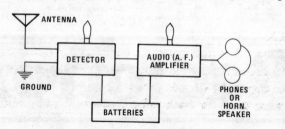

TRF

The tuned-radio frequency (TRF) set was much-used for broadcast reception in the mid-to-latter 1920's, and even 1930's. The incoming radio signal was amplified by vacuum tube amplifier stages tuned to the station frequency. It was then detected and amplified:

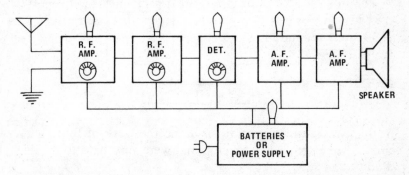

This gave good loudspeaker volume. Most of the early sets had separate tuning knobs on each R. F. amplifier and on the detector. This made finding a station something of a challenge, like dialing a 3-combination safe. When better amplifier tubes were made, the tuning condensers were all ganged together to one tuning knob; some of the delicate adjustability was lost in the name of convenience.

NEUTRODYNE

TRF sets often oscillated (squealed) because the old triode tubes tended to feed R.F. energy back to their own inputs. This bothersome effect was cancelled by special feed-back circuits. The best neutralizing circuit was Hazeltine's "Neutrodyne", so it was used by many radio builders. Thus, a "Neutrodyne" receiver is just a TRF using these especially good neutralizing circuits.

REFLEX

Vacuum tubes and batteries were very expensive in the early days. In order to save tubes and battery drain, ways were found to make each tube do two jobs. In common reflex sets, the same tubes were used for both radio-frequency and audio-frequency duties:

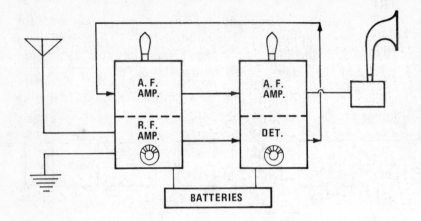

In this circuit we see two tubes doing the work of four. These circuits were somewhat touchy, and were very hard to troubleshoot.

SUPERHETERODYNE

The superheterodyne circuit was invented in 1918 by the brilliant Edwin H. Armstrong. It was clearly superior to TRF, but took more tubes and was tied up by RCA's patent position until 1930. Superheterodyne circuitry eliminated "tracking" problems found in tuning the TRF circuit. The idea is to convert any incoming signal to one frequency (called the "intermediate" frequency) so that most of the amplification is done in I.F. amplifier stages that are always tuned to one frequency:

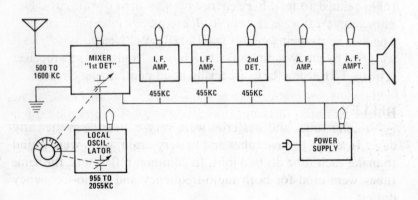

This is the basic circuit used in almost all radios today. It has high selectivity, high sensitivity and is very stable (drift-free). Very often, on higher-priced sets, a TRF amplifier stage will be added ahead of the mixer to improve tuning even further, particularly by eliminating "image" effect. Images occur because the I.F. amplifier can respond to signals at the local oscillator frequency plus 455KC, as well as at the desired L.O. frequency minus 455KC. The TRF stage will cut out any signals that might give image problems, preselecting only the desired frequencies.

SUPERREGENERATION

The superregenerative circuit is by far the most sensitive of all one-tube receiver circuits. The circuit breaks into and out of self-oscillation at random times, making a "hiss" in the headphones. When a signal (even a very weak one) is present, the circuit breaks into self-oscillation in coordination with the signal, hence the signal is heard in the headset. It has disadvantages because it is not very selective (doesn't tune sharply) and it bothers nearby receivers by radiating its own signal.

AM vs. FM

All early voice transmissions were by amplitude modulation (AM), in which the amplitude (strength) of the transmitted signal was varied in accordance with the audio signal being sent. In 1933 Armstrong perfected FM, in which the frequency is varied in accordance with the audio signal being sent. FM has the advantage of being almost immune to electrical interference, and has other characteristics making it ideal for high-fidelity broadcasts. Because it takes up more frequency, FM must operate in higher frequency bands. Pre-World War II FM broadcasting was in the 44-50 Mc band, but postwar FM was moved to the present 88-108 Mc slot. The AM band (500-1600 Kc) is noisier and does not have the quality, but its distance range is much greater.

Basically an FM receiver is a superheterodyne like an AM set. However, it has a different tuning range, a different I.F. frequency (typically 10.7Mc) and a different detector circuit. Expensive sets have a limiter stage and an FM discriminator detector; moderately-priced sets have a "ratio detector"; real cheapos have superregenerative receiver circuits.

SSB

Single-sideband (SSB) was just coming into the picture by 1950. It is an ingeneous scheme for conserving our limited frequency resources. If you look at an AM signal, you'll find that it has an upper-frequency "sideband", a "carrier" and a lower-frequency "sideband". Special circuit techniques let us take out the carrier and one sideband reconstituting them at the receiving end. This means that less than half the frequency bandwidth and one-fourth the radio transmitter energy is needed to send a voice signal over the crowded airwaves.

KELLER-FULLER
"RADIETTE"

AVALON
"MODEL A"

JACKSON-BELL "62"

ECHOPHONE "S-3"

PIONEERS: 1929-30 "CATHEDRALS"

We hope this book has been interesting to you, and that it has increased your appetite for information. We invite you to keep in touch with us for bulletins on new Vintage Radio books and information services. As of this printing, other members of the Vintage Radio series are:

Vintage Radio; a pictorial history of wireless and radio from 1887 through 1929. 263 pages. Our "basic" book.

Radio Collector's Guide; data book with 50,000 pieces of information on 4,000 models built by 1,100 manufacturers, 1921-1932, 264 pages.

H. Gernsback's 1927 Radio Encyclopedia; the best available picture of radio as it was in the early days, with explanations of old terms like "variometer" and "coherer", 175 pages, near-replica of the original.

Most-Often-Needed 1926-1938 Radio Diagrams; Morris Beitman's Supreme Publications book reproduced with his permission. 240 pages.

We also have other special printings and offer other publishers' books that we think will interest you.

Please write and tell us what you like or don't like about this book, and what you'd like to see in future books. After all, these books are written for you. Just drop a line to Vintage Radio, P.O. Box 2045, Palos Verdes Peninsula, California 90274.

Morgan McMahon has spent most of his life living in the future. He became a radio amateur back in the days when the local "ham" was considered the neighborhood nut. In World War II he worked with advanced electronic systems. He went into solid-state research after earning his Master's degree at the University of California. He taught the first transistor course given in the West, at UCLA.

Mr. McMahon's career in industry has revolved around new business ventures and advanced technology. He helped start one semiconductor company. He then set up diode, transistor and integrated circuit operations for a major electronic manufacturer. He was Chief Scientist for the largest U.S. manufacturer of electronic parts. He is now a consultant.

Some years ago Mr. McMahon became interested in the history of electronics. To his surprise, the early days of this field were not at all well recorded. Mr. McMahon enlisted the willing help of historians, collectors, historical societies, technical publishers and old-line manufacturers to assemble Vintage Radio. His aim is to help preserve this piece of our heritage in an enjoyable way, in a series of readable books.